John Fost... ...nt
much of h... ...ce
the junior te... ...

He was a teacher for over twenty years before becoming a full-time writer. He is the country's most prolific anthologist, having compiled over a hundred anthologies of children's poetry. His bestselling books include *Twinkle Twinkle Chocolate Bar* and the poetry collections illustrated by Korky Paul, such as *Dinosaur Poems* and *Dragon Poems*.

John has also written twelve books of his own poetry. He says that he first started to make up poems to amuse his children on long car journeys and hopes that his poetry helps children to think about themselves and the world they live in. His book *The Poetry Chest* contains more than 250 of his own poems.

John is also one of Britain's leading poetry performers for children, well known for his performances as a dancing dinosaur and a rapping granny.

John has two grown-up sons and two grandchildren, Evie and Louis, and now lives with his wife Chris in Oxfordshire. He remains a fervent supporter of poetry and of Carlisle United.

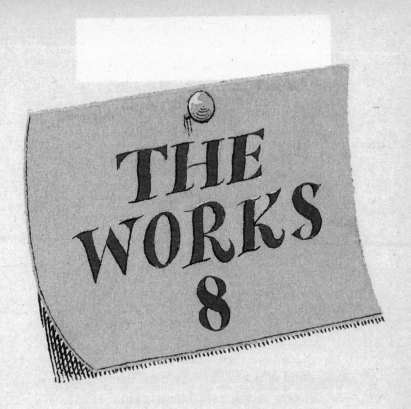

THE WORKS 8

Every shape, style and
form of poem that you
will ever need for the
Literacy Hour

Chosen by John Foster

MACMILLAN CHILDREN'S BOOKS

First published 2009 by Macmillan Children's Books
a division of Macmillan Publishers Limited
20 New Wharf Road, London N1 9RR
Basingstoke and Oxford
Associated companies throughout the world
www.panmacmillan.com

ISBN 978-0-330-46407-9

Typeset by Intype Libra Limited
Printed and bound in the UK by CPI Mackays, Chatham ME5 8TD

Contents

Contents

Autobiographical poems

B is for . . .
Ballads

C is for . . .
Calligrams

Chain poems

Chants

Contents

Contents

Concrete poems

Conversation poems

Counting poems

Couplets

Contents

D is for . . .

Diamond poems

Diary poems

E is for . . .

Elegies

Epigrams

Epitaphs

Contents

Contents

Interviews

J is for . . .
Joke poems

K is for . . .
Kennings

L is for . . .
Letter poems

Contents

M is for . . .

Metaphor poems

Contents

N is for . . .
Nonsense poems

O is for . . .
Odes

P is for . . .
Parodies

Postcard poems

Poster poems

Contents

Q is for . . .

Question poems

Contents

R is for . . .

Raps

Recipe poems

Rhyming poems

Riddles

Rondelets

Contents

S is for . . .

Shape poems

Simile poems

Sonnets

Spells

Contents

Contents

V is for . . .
Villanelles

W is for . . .
Warnings

Wishes

Wordplay poems

Contents

Introduction

Welcome to *The Works 8* – an alphabet of poetry forms. Poems can be written in many different ways, and this book provides an introduction to the variety of forms that poets use today.

Some of the forms are traditional, such as the ballad, which dates back to the time when poems were spoken or sung. Others are traditional forms that have been borrowed from other languages. The haiku, for example, is one of the most ancient forms of Japanese poetry, while the sonnet was first used in Italy and came to England around 1520. The triolet, the villanelle and the rondelet are old French verse-forms.

More recently, a number of verse-forms have been invented and popularized by individual poets. The nineteenth-century American poet Adelaide Crapsey invented the cinquain, and Edmund Clerihew Bentley invented the clerihew. The limerick was made popular in the nineteenth century by Edward Lear, who also contributed to the development of nonsense verse.

In modern times, poets have experimented widely with different forms, writing poems in the style of diary entries and advertisements, letters and postcards. They have also continued the trend to borrow forms by using the rap form, which originated in African-American culture.

The range of poetic forms is very wide, from poems written as insults and as interviews to tongue-twisters and univocalics – poems that use only words containing only one of the five vowels.

Introduction

We've even invented a new form especially for this book. In order to have an entry for every letter of the alphabet, for X we've invented the X-ray poem.

We hope that you'll enjoying reading and learning about the different forms that can be used and, if you want to experiment yourselves, trying some of the ideas for writing your own poems that are suggested in a separate section at the back of the book.

John Foster

A is for . . .

Acrostics

An acrostic is a poem in which certain letters of a word in each line together form a word or a number of words.

Waterfall

Water, white as a veil,
Arches across rocks, falls,
Tosses in turbulent torrents,
Excites, enchants, enthrals.
Rushing and racing it roars, pours,
Furious and fast. Fantastic it spills.
Amazingly splintered it thrills.
Leaps, light-sparkling and lithe.
Lands and lingers in limpid, lace-edged pools.

Cynthia Rider

Cathedral

Come into this quiet place where
Angels carved in stone look down on
Tombs of noble lords and ladies.
Here are stained-glass windows to delight the
Eye and tell us tales of long ago – here the Great West
Door and there an eagle spreads its wings. Here are
Rows and rows of seats and high above each aisle
Arches soar. Come into this quiet place.
Listen to its peace.

June Crebbin

Whoosh! Cheetah!

A member of the Cat family
and sucH a speedy sprintah.
It racEs across Africa's plains
to catch antelopE and zebrah.
Can climb a Tree with agilitee,
and is All quicksilver speed. A dashah.
Whoosh! CheetaH!

Wes Magee

The Bard

TWelfth Night
As You LIke It
OtheLlo
Romeo and JuLiet
The Merry WIves of Windsor
HAmlet
The CoMedy of Errors

A MidSummer-Night's Dream
MacbetH
Julius CAesar
King Lear
Anthony and ClEopatra
The Taming of the Shrew
The TemPest
HEnry V
CoriolAnus
Richard III
All's Well That Ends Well

Derek Stuart

Riddle-me-right

Card magic is mighty easy to me, so are legerdemain and mesmerisM
Outlandish are my powers and my personality and my paraphernaliA
Nothing is to me impossible. No, nothing. Absolutely no thinG
Just try and explain my flashy, trashy, trumpery tricks. Try! I
Usually defy all measly, mundane explanations. Mysterious magiC
Rodomontade is my reason, my rhetoric, my rationale, my trade. I
Excel at deception, at disappearance, at inducing doubt. Am I A
¿Riddling mountebank, dear reader, or a miraculous master magiciaN?

Gerard Benson

Acrostics

Acrostics
Clearly
Reveal
Obsessional
Sequencing
Tendencies
In
Clever
So-and-sos

Coral Rumble

Adverb poems

An adverb is a word that tells you more about a verb by describing it. An adverb poem is a poem which focuses on one adverb or several adverbs.

Quietly

Quietly the fox stalks its prey.
Quietly the cat sleeps in the hay.
Quietly the man sits in his chair.
Quietly the mermaid combs her hair.

Quietly the swan glides down the river.
Quietly the snake begins to slither.
Quietly moves the moon – but most quiet of all
Is the thinking I've done watching leaves fall.

Aenaone Tickler

Suddenly

Suddenly
felt a hand gripping my wrist
reminds me
how a prisoner must feel
as the handcuffs are snapped on

Erica Stewart

How wickedly the wolf grins

How wickedly the wolf grins:
its bared teeth two rows of unsheathed daggers.

Erica Stewart

In the Rush-hour Traffic Jam

Wearily, drearily, stiff with strain
I stared through the windows streaked with rain
At the truck in front and the bus to the rear,
Fearing the traffic just never would clear.

Moodily, broodily turning my gaze
Away from the stifling blue exhaust haze,
Grumbling as miserably, creeping like snails,
Commuters inched homeward, noses to tails.

Strangely, amazingly there to the right
I noticed the most incongruous sight
Of an elderly gentleman, relaxed at the wheel,
The warmth of whose smile I could virtually feel.

Unhappily, snappily, ill-mannered lout,
I said, 'What are you so happy about?'
'Son,' he said gently, 'try being like me
When you find that you're somewhere you don't want to be.

'Gently, intently, I empty my mind
And over displeasure I draw down a blind
Frustration flows out, mem'ries flood in
And I'm back to my boyhood away from the din.

'Lazily, daisily in meadow I lie,
Exploring cloud mountains in summer's blue sky,
Warmed by the sun and cooled by the breeze,
Lulled by the birdsong filling the trees.

'Slowly, silently parting the sedge
That's growing down to the water's edge,
I see shadowy fish in sparkling rill.
That's where memories take me still.'

Beguilingly, smilingly with twinkling eye,
He waved a hand in brief goodbye,
Leaving me lost in remembered dreams
Of summers and sunshine, meadows and streams.

Philip C. Gross

Slowly

Slowly the coming down
For breakfast, pulling back
The curtains in each room, the opening
Of windows just a little (*Have to
Let the air in*), asking me
To pick the letters up
To save him bending, slowly
Reading them, his grey lips
Moving in his beard
To shape each word, then slowly
Walking to his desk
And standing there in front of
Grandma's photo, saying
*Well, old girl, how goes it?
Here's another day!*

Slowly goes everything
In Grandpa's house,
But beautifully too, just right.
He likes us coming.
Mum says it can't go on
Much longer, talks about
Arrangements, but I don't see
Why. The thing to do is
Just what Grandpa says you should,
To take thing slowly, very
Slowly till they stop.

John Mole

Advertisement poems

An advertisement poem is one written in the form of an advertisement.

Wanted!!

Lead singer for new Super Group
Ability to sing an advantage but NOT ESSENTIAL!
However, must be able to:
Pout your lips
Strut on stage
Act your shoe size
Not your age
Wiggle hips
Jump about
Make the young girls
Scream and shout
Move and groove
Play air-guitar
But most of all
Act like a star.

If you think this could be you
Call now for an interview.

Phone: 800–242

Richard Caley

Di Knows What's Best for Dinosaurs

Di knows what's best for dinosaurs.
For glistening scales and sharpened claws,
Visit Di's 4 Dinosaurs.

Whether you're two tonnes or ten tonnes,
Let our giant crane take the strain
And hoist you into our lake
For a refreshing dip.

Then visit our shower hall
For a steam-clean and a power-scrub
Before enjoying a scale-polishing session
In our polishing parlour.

Sharpen up your claws and spikes
On our knife-grinding machines,
Or practise your tail-whipping
In our fully equipped gym.

Smarten up your snarl
With a full facial
That will leave you looking grim and gruesome.

And have a snack in our gourmet café.
Our specialities include
Spiced shrubs for vegetarians
And mammoth pie for the meat-eater.

Di knows what's best for dinosaurs.
For glistening scales and sharpened claws
Visit Di's 4 Dinosaurs.

A dinosaur whatever their size
Will never forget a visit to Di's!

John Foster

Advertisement

Are your children peaky and thin?
Too many late nights? Too much telly?
Forest air and a fattening diet
   Will very soon put things right.

A week or two at Sweetmeat Cottage
Is bound to make them scrumptiously chubby.
Children just love my gingerbread house,
   My liquorice doors and chimneys.

There's everything here to delight a child,
And one kind lady to see to their needs –
For I love children, tasty little darlings!
   Apply without delay.

Cornelius Doyle

Lonely Heart

WANTED:
Knight in shining armour for my mum. V. pretty, but
not so v. pretty in the morning.
Age (hers): N.O.Y.B.
Hobbies include: Wound dressing, cooking meals
and throwing in bin, biscuit eating (to Olympic level),
asking 'Do I look fat to you?', building castles
(sand only).
Seeking: Non-squeamish male who can plan Civil War
battles, write convincing sick notes and revive
hamsters and goldfish.
Would prefer: Professional footballer willing to
spoil ungrateful and unruly children.
Would settle for: Someone to make Mum laugh
like drain or ticklish princess.

Lindsay MacRae

Alphabet poems

An alphabet poem is a poem in which the poet uses the letters of the alphabet to give a pattern to the poem. Some alphabet poems play with the sounds of the letters.

An Alphabet of Questions

Have Angleworms attractive homes?
Do Bumblebees have brains?
Do Caterpillars carry combs?
Do Dodos dote on drains?
Can Eels elude electric earls?
Do Flatfish fish for flats?
Are Grigs agreeable to girls?
Do Hares have hunting hats?
Do ices make an Ibex ill?
Do Jackdaws jug their jam?
Do Kites kiss all the kids they kill?
Do Llamas live on lamb?
Will Moles molest a mounted mink?
Do Newts deny the news?
Are Oysters boisterous when they drink?
Do Parrots prowl in pews?
Do Quakers get their quills from quails?
Do Rabbits rob on roads?
Are Snakes supposed to sneer at snails?
Do Tortoises eat toads?
Can Unicorns perform on horns?

15

Do Vipers value veal?
Do Weasels weep when fast asleep?
Can Xylophagans squeal?
Do Yaks in packs invite attacks?
Are Zebras full of zeal?

Charles Edward Carryl

An A–Z of Pop Groups

Arm Band
Creeping Daughters
Egg Flops
Giant Heart
International Jets
Kissing Llama
Mutant Noise
Oblong Peanut
Queer Rabbit
Silver Tongues
Ugly Vicar
Wet Xmas
Yellow Zebra

Wes Magee

A Letter to the Alphabet

Dear Alphabet,

I'd like to say, thanks, for the words you give away. From Aadvarks to Zebras, from millions to noughts your twenty-six letters calculate thoughts. I can read what is written, I can write what I say, I can picture with words in every way.

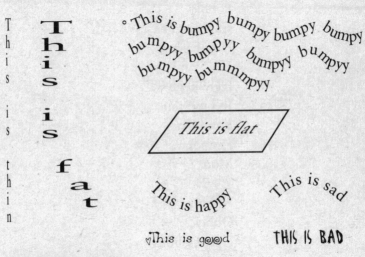

This is bumpy bumpy bumpy bumpy bumpyy bumpyy bumpyy bumpyy bumpyy bummmpyy

This is flat

This is happy

This is sad

This is good

THIS IS BAD

and this

This is writing on a wall

is the alphabet
ABCDEFGHIJKLM
NOPQRSTUVWXYZ

that says it all.

Julie Holder

Alphabotsie, Alphaboodle

Archer-varcher
Booga
Chrimble
Doo-dah-day

Eggy-peggy
Fobble
Gabbly-gub
Hoo-ha-hey

Iggly-jiggly
Joo-joo-jam
Karamba
Limpopo
Moo

Nobbly
Obbly
Pipsidissimus
Quiggly
Riggly
Stroggly
Too

Umpop
Veega
Woggle-woggle

Xmiff
Yogo
Zoohoohoo

Matt Black

Autobiographical poems

An autobiographical poem is a poem based on the poet's personal experience.

What It Was Like

The day my bike brakes failed
on a steep hill near home
I squeezed and squeezed them
tight up to the handle-bars
and nothing happened
as I sped against the wind
with terrified eyes clamped shut.

It was like when I had this dream
of switching off my radio
and when I felt the click
a voice I recognised
but couldn't put a name or face to
just went on and on and on
as if it knew I wasn't going to wake.

John Mole

Skating at Night

And in the frosty season, when the sun
Was set, and visible for many a mile
The cottage windows through the twilight blaz'd,
I heeded not the summons. Clear and loud
The village clock tolled six; I wheeled about
Proud and exulting, like an untired horse,
That cares not for his home. All shod with steel,
We hissed along the polished ice in games
Confederate, imitative of the chase
And woodland pleasures, the resounding horn,
The pack loud bellowing, and the hunted hare.
So through the darkness and the cold we flew,
And not a voice was idle. With the din,
Meanwhile, the precipices rang aloud;
The leafless trees and every icy crag
Tinkled like iron; while the distant hills
Into the tumult sent an alien sound
Of melancholy, not unnoticed; while the stars,
Eastward were sparkling clear, and in the west
The orange sky of evening died away.

William Wordsworth

Left Out

It feels as if pins
Are pricking my eyes.
My face is burning hot.
A firework is trying
To go off inside me.
My feet are glued to the spot.
My hands are rocks in my pockets.
I want to run away.
But my legs are rooted to the ground
Like trees. I have to stay
And listen
To everyone calling me names
And not letting me
Join in with their games.

Celia Warren

Goodbye

My holidays were spent with Gran.
She was very small and very old.
In the evening she'd tell stories
Of when she was even smaller,
And the saddest one she told
Was about her baby brother
Who they knew was going to die,
So all her family stood in line
To kiss him for the last time
And say goodbye.

She let me do things not allowed at home.
She cooked custard for breakfast
And brought it on a tray to me in bed.
She let me feed the pigeons on a window ledge.
But the best was the day when I said
How I'd like to make a bed in the bath.
So she tied up the taps,
Fetched blankets and sheets,
Lined it with pillows
And I slept there for the week.

But I outgrew Gran.
As I grew taller she became the child.
My visits grew fewer.
Then one day when I called
She opened the door and smiled,
'Hello, John. It is John, isn't it?'
'No, Gran. I'm the other one.'
(How could she mistake me for my brother?)

I was too busy growing up for childish games.
Too busy to drop by.
When I had the time,
Her time had run out.
It was too late to say goodbye.

Pat Moon

B is for . . .

Ballads

A ballad is a type of poem or song which tells a story. It is usually written in a number of short verses, often in simple, colloquial language. The first ballads were spoken or sung rather than written down. They told stories of love and heroism, mystery and adventure.

Brennan on the Moor

It's of a fearless highwayman a story I will tell,
His name was Willie Brennan and in Ireland he did dwell.
'Twas on the Kilworth mountains he began a wild career,
And many a noble gentleman before him shook with fear.

Crying Brennan's on the moor! Brennan's on the moor!
So bold and undaunted stood Bill Brennan on the moor.

'Twas on the King's own highway now Brennan he sat
   down,
He met the Mayor of Cashel just five miles out of town.
The Mayor he looked at Brennan and, 'I think now, boy,'
   says he,
'Your name is Willie Brennan, you must come along with
   me.'

Now Brennan's wife was going down town provisions for
to buy,
And she seen Willie taken, ah sure she began to cry,
'Hand me ten pennies!' and sure just as he spoke,
She handed him a blunderbuss from underneath her cloak.

Brennan had his blunderbuss, my story I'll unfold,
He caused the Mayor of Cashel to deliver up his gold.
Five thousand pounds were offered for his apprehension
there,
But Brennan and the pedlar to the mountain did repair.

Now Brennan is an outlaw upon a mountain high,
With Infantry and Cavalry to catch him they did try.
He laughed at them, he scorned at them until, it is said,
A false-hearted woman caused him to lose his head.

They hung him at the crossroads, in chains he swung and
died.
Some say in the midnight hour you still can see him ride.
You'll see him with his blunderbuss. And in the midnight
chill
Along the King's own highway rides Willie Brennan still.

Anon.

Lord Ullin's Daughter

A chieftain to the Highlands bound
Cries, 'Boatman, do not tarry!
And I'll give thee a silver pound
To row us o'er the ferry!'

'Now who be ye, would cross Loch Gyle,
This dark and stormy water?'
'O I'm the chief of Ulva's Isle,
And this, Lord Ullin's daughter.

'And fast before her father's men
Three days we've fled together,
For should he find us in the glen,
My blood would stain the heather.

'His horsemen hard behind us ride –
Should they our steps discover,
Then who will cheer my bonny bride
When they have slain her lover?'

Out spoke the hardy Highland wight,
'I'll go, my chief, I'm ready;
It is not for your silver bright,
But for your winsome lady –

'And, by my word, the bonny bird
In danger shall not tarry;
So though the waves are raging white,
I'll row you o'er the ferry.'

By this the storm grew loud apace,
The water-wraith was shrieking;
And in scowl of heaven each face
Grew dark as they were speaking.

But still as wilder blew the wind,
And as the night grew drearer,
Adown the glen rode armèd men,
Their trampling sounded nearer.

'O haste thee, haste!' the lady cries,
'Though tempests round us gather;
I'll meet the raging of the skies,
But not an angry father.'

The boat has left a stormy land,
A stormy sea before her –
When O! too strong for human hand
The tempest gathered o'er her.

And still they rowed amidst the roar
Of waters fast prevailing:
Lord Ullin reached that fatal shore –
His wrath was changed to wailing.

For, sore dismayed, through storm and shade
His child he did discover;
One lovely hand she stretched for aid,
And one was round her lover.

'Come back! Come back!' he cried in grief,
'Across the stormy water,
And I'll forgive your Highland chief,
My daughter! – O, my daughter!'

'Twas vain: the loud waves lashed the shore,
Return or aid preventing;
The waters wild went o'er his child,
And he was left lamenting.

Thomas Campbell

La Belle Dame Sans Merci

'O what can ail thee, Knight-at-arms,
Alone and palely loitering?
The sedge is wither'd from the lake,
And no birds sing.

'O what can ail thee, Knight-at-arms,
So haggard and so woebegone?
The squirrel's granary is full,
And the harvest's done.

'I see a lily on thy brow
With anguish moist and fever dew,
And on thy cheek a fading rose
Fast withereth too.'

'I met a lady in the meads
Full beautiful – a faery's child,
Her hair was long, her foot was light,
And her eyes were wild.

'I made a garland for her head,
And bracelets too, and fragrant zone;
She look'd at me as she did love,
And made sweet moan.

'I set her on my pacing steed,
And nothing else saw all day long,
For sidelong would she bend and sing
A faery's song.

'She found me roots of relish sweet,
And honey wild and manna dew,
And sure in language strange she said,
"I love thee true."

'She took me to her elfin grot,
And there she wept and sigh'd full sore;
And there I shut her wild wild eyes
With kisses four.

'And there she lullèd me asleep,
And there I dream'd – Ah! woe betide!
The latest dream I ever dream'd
On the cold hill's side.

'I saw pale kings and princes too,
Pale warriors, death-pale were they all:
Who cried – "La belle Dame sans merci
Hath thee in thrall!"

'I saw their starv'd lips in the gloam
With horrid warning gapèd wide,
And I awoke and found me here
On the cold hill's side.

'And this is why I sojourn here
Alone and palely loitering,
Though the sedge is wither'd from the lake,
And no birds sing.'

John Keats

The Ballad of Homeless Jack

You'll pass him in the doorway,
you'll see him in the street,
with a blanket on his shoulders,
second-hand shoes on his feet.

You'll hear him squeeze from his whistle
a tune that's cracked and strange.
You'll see his hat left hopefully
to gather up your change.

Nobody stops to speak to him,
nobody catches his eye,
from the stream of hurrying people
who pass so swiftly by.

With a grubby bundle in his hand
and a charity coat on his back,
you'll meet him all across the land.
His name is Homeless Jack.

Now some say Jack is lazy,
and some say Jack is bad,
and some say Jack's a hopeless case,
a junkie, drunkard, mad.

But Jack says he's a human being,
not far from me or you.
He sees no point, he has no hope,
so what is Jack to do,

but sit upon his blanket
and let the world walk on
till life at last deserts him
and even dreams are gone?

And maybe as we hurry by
and look the other way,
we know that in the doorway
it could be us one day.

So why not spare for Homeless Jack
a word, a nod, a grin,
to hold the tide of helplessness
from coldly creeping in?

Tony Mitton

C is for . . .

Calligrams

A calligram is a poem in which the handwriting (the calligraphy), the formation of the letters or the typeface used, represents an aspect of the poem's subject.

Calligrams

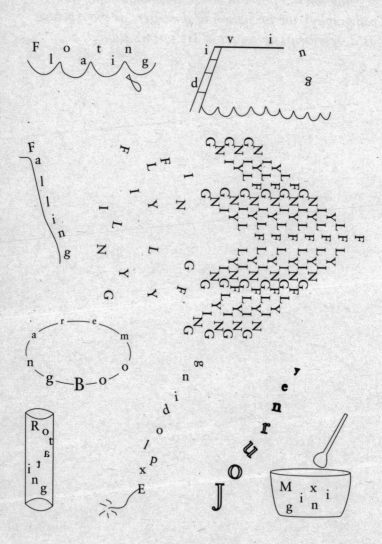

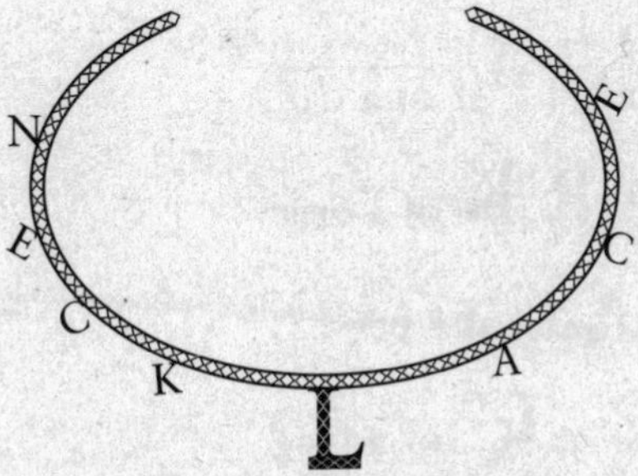

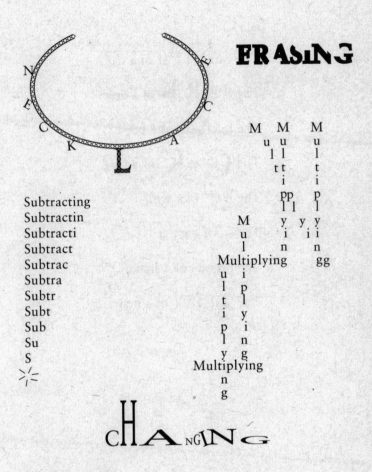

ERASING

M M M
u u u
l l l
t t t
i i
pp p
l l l
M y y y
u i i i
l n n
Multiplying gg
u i
l p
t l
i y
p i
l n
y g
Multiplying
n
g

Subtracting
Subtractin
Subtracti
Subtract
Subtrac
Subtra
Subtr
Subt
Sub
Su
S

CHANGING

MAG

Ian Bland

Animal Noises

The pur^{r}$_{r}$ r ^{r}$_{r}$^{r} of a cat

The B A R K of a dog

The buz ^{z}$_{z}$z ^{z}$_{z}$^{z} of a bee

The CROAK of a frog

The ho^{w}^{l} of a wolf

The cheep of a wren

The hisssssss of a snake

The SQUAWK of a hen

Derek Stuart

Rhythm Machine

Soft and **humming**

LOUD and strumming – listen to that NEAT refrain!

Add a TRUMPET

And a  kit –

Why not change the B
      E
        A
          T again?

UP
THE *VOLUME*

Eardrum priser,  POP GROUP
SyntheSIZER!

Trevor Harvey

Chain poems

A chain poem is one in which each line or each verse is linked to the previous one, like the links in a chain.

This Is the Key

This is the Key of the Kingdom
In that Kingdom is a city;
In that city is a town;
In that town there is a street;
In that street there winds a lane;
In that lane there is a yard;
In that yard there is a house;
In that house there waits a room;
In that room an empty bed;
And on that bed a basket –
A Basket of Sweet Flowers;
   Of Flowers, of Flowers;
   A Basket of Sweet Flowers.

Flowers in a Basket;
Basket on the bed;
Bed in the chamber;
Chamber in the house;
House in the weedy yard;
Yard in the winding lane;
Lane in the broad street;
Street in the high town;
Town in the city;
City in the Kingdom –
This is the Key of the Kingdom.
 Of the Kingdom this is the Key.

Anon.

If a Jackal Bothers You

If a jackal bothers you, show it a hyena,
If a hyena bothers you, show it a lion,
If a lion bothers you, show it an elephant,
If an elephant bothers you, show it a hunter,
If a hunter bothers you, show him a snake,
If a snake bothers you, show it a stick,
If a stick bothers you, show it a fire,
If a fire bothers you, show it a river,
If a river bothers you, show it the wind,
If the wind bothers you, show it God.

Traditional African

The Castle on the Hill

On the hill there stands a castle.
Round the castle there is a moat.
Over the moat there is a bridge.
Beyond the bridge there is a door.
Through the door there is a courtyard.
Across the courtyard stands a tower.
Inside the tower there is a staircase.
Up the staircase there is a door.
Across the door iron bolts are drawn.
Behind the door a young girl sleeps . . .

On the hill there stands a castle.
Round the castle there is a moat . . .

John Foster

The Nest That Jack Built

This is the nest that Jack built.

This is the branch of tangled twigs
That cradle the nest that Jack built.

These are the rooks, the noisy neighbours
That kept him company in his labours
Along the branch of tangled twigs
That cradle the nest that Jack built.

These are the nests in several trees
That weather the wind and wave in the breeze
And house the rooks, the noisy neighbours
That kept him company in his labours
Along the branch of tangled twigs
That cradle the nest that Jack built.

These are the eggs – and this is the spring!
And this is the caw and noisy clack
Which makes the song the birds all sing –
The jackdaws, rooks, his mate and Jack:
Among the nests in several trees
Which weather the wind and wave in the breeze
And house the rooks, the noisy neighbours
That kept him company on his labours
Along the branch of tangled twigs
That cradle the nest that Jack built.

Richard Tysoe

There Was a Man of Double Deed

There was a man of double deed
Who sowed his garden full of seed.
Then the seeds began to grow,
like a garden full of snow.
Then the snow began to melt,
like a ship without a belt.
Then the ship began to sail,
like a bird without a tail.
Then the bird began to fly,
like an eagle in the sky.
Then the sky began to roar,
like a lion at the door.
Then the door began to crack,
like a stick across my back.
Then my back began to smart,
like a penknife in my heart.
Then my heart began to bleed,
like a needle full of thread.
Then the thread began to rot,
like a turnip in the pot.
Then the pot began to boil,
like a bottle full of oil.
Then the oil began to settle,
like the water in the kettle.
When the kettle boils no more,
Out goes the man to fight a war.

Anon.

For Want of a Nail

For want of a nail, the shoe was lost;
For want of a shoe, the horse was lost;
For want of a horse, the rider was lost;
For want of a rider, the battle was lost;
For want of a battle, the kingdom was lost:
And all for the want of a horseshoe nail.

Anon.

Chants

A chant is a type of performance poem that is written to be spoken. Chants have a strong rhythm and often also use repetition and rhyme to create their effect.

Chick, Chick, Chatterman

Chick, chick, chatterman
How much are your geese?
Chick, chick, chatterman
Five cents apiece.
Chick, chick, chatterman
That's too dear.
Chick, chick, chatterman
Get out of here.

Anon.

Policeman, Policeman

Policeman, policeman
   don't catch me!
Catch that boy
   behind that tree.
He stole apples,
   I stole none;
Put him in the jailhouse,
   just for fun.

Anon.

The Song of the Homeworkers

To be read or chanted with increasing velocity

Homework moanwork
Cross it out and groanwork
Homework neatwork
Keeps you off the streetwork
Homework moanwork
Cross it out and groanwork
Homework roughwork
When you've had about enoughwork
Homework moanwork
Cross it out and groanwork
Homework dronework
Do it on your ownwork
Homework moanwork
Cross it out and groanwork
Homework gloomwork
Gaze around the roomwork
Homework moanwork
Cross it out and groanwork
Homework guesswork
Book is in a messwork
Homework moanwork
Cross it out and groanwork
Homework rushwork
Do it on the buswork

Homework moanwork
Cross it out and groanwork
Homework hatework
Hand your book in latework
Homework moanwork
Cross it out and groan groan GROANWORK!

Trevor Millum

Trick or Treat

Trick or treat, trick or treat
Pumpkins light up every street
Trick or treat, trick or treat
Witches watch and gremlins greet
Trick or treat, trick or treat
Skeletons and vampires meet
Trick or treat, trick or treat

Halloween, Halloween
Ghosts and ghouls, glowing green
Halloween, Halloween
Werewolves hairy, scary, mean
Halloween, Halloween
Mummies lurch and monsters lean
Halloween, Halloween

Paul Cookson

The Witches' Chant

(from Macbeth*)*

Round about the cauldron go;
In the poison'd entrails throw.
Toad, that under cold stone
Days and nights has thirty-one
Swelter'd venom sleeping got,
Boil thou first i' the charmed pot.

Double, double, toil and trouble;
Fire burn; and cauldron bubble.

Fillet of a fenny snake,
In the cauldron boil and bake;
Eye of newt, and toe of frog,
Wool of bat, and tongue of dog,
Adder's fork, and blind-worm's sting,
Lizard's leg, and howlet's wing,
For a charm of powerful trouble,
Like a hell-broth boil and bubble.

Double, double, toil and trouble;
Fire burn; and cauldron bubble.

William Shakespeare

Cinquains

A cinquain is a type of syllable poem, which was invented by an American poet called Adelaide Crapsey. It consists of five lines, containing twenty-two syllables in the following pattern: 2–4–6–8–2.

The Warning

Just now,
Out of the strange
Still dusk . . . as strange, as still . . .
A white moth flew. Why am I grown
So cold?

Adelaide Crapsey

Amaze

I know
Not these my hands
And yet I think there was
A woman like me once had hands
Like these.

Adelaide Crapsey

November Night

Listen . . .
With faint dry sound
Like steps of passing ghosts,
The leaves, frost-crisped, break from the trees
And fall.

Adelaide Crapsey

Seasonal Cinquains

Autumn
Tinge of henna
Crackling fires and leaves
Deep rooting tick of biding time
Digging.

Winter
Stiff morning air
Cracked ice on sleeping seeds
Frosty breath shiver-shudders words
Waiting.

Spring air
Fairy-wing breeze
Lifting blossom petals
Weightless whispering of summer
Stirring.

Summer
Claiming a crown
Exploding wild colours
In a frenzy of patterning
Clapping.

Coral Rumble

The River Cinquains

Dawn

Daybreak:
Between grey rocks,
Silently it wells up
With the force of blood from a wound:
Water.

Morning

Moorland:
Purple heather:
Early sun lights the stream:
Rushing, chattering, swift with fish,
Sparkling.

Afternoon

Townscape:
Water reflects
Grey brickwork, dull windows.
Fishermen stare. The river moves
Slowly.

Evening

Salt-marsh:
Under lead skies
The water slides away.
From the damp banks of sand a few
Birds call.

Night

Moon shines
On open sea:
The swell gleams with silver
And on a distant shore the first
Waves break.

Nigel Cox

Sad School Cinquains

DIFFERENT

Jodie
Is different
And so she sits alone.
She never looks up from her desk
To smile.

QUIET

Miss Law
Looks sad today,
She is quiet and still.
Her grown-up world has followed her
To school.

TESTS

In tests
I get low marks.
My teacher says, 'Well tried,'
But her words don't mean anything
To me.

SOMETIMES

Sometimes
They just stare hard,
Nudge each other and smile;
And I pretend that I don't care –
Sometimes.

STANDING

Standing
By the office,
In trouble once again,
Makes my heart bash against my ribs
Loudly.

Coral Rumble

Clerihews

A clerihew is a four-line verse consisting of two rhyming couplets. The first line of a clerihew contains the name of the person who is the subject of the poem. It is named after the man who invented it, Edmund Clerihew Bentley.

Edmund Clerihew Bentley

Edmund Clerihew Bentley
Said, 'I recently
Had nothing better to do,
So I invented the clerihew.'

John Foster

Sir Christopher Wren

Sir Christopher Wren
Said, 'I am going to dine with some men.
If anybody calls
Say I am designing St Paul's.'

E. C. Bentley

Alfred, Lord Tennyson

Alfred, Lord Tennyson
Lived upon venison;
Not cheap, I fear,
Because venison's deer.

E. C. Bentley

David Attenborough

David Attenborough
Crawls through habitat and burrow
Seeking a clue
To the animals' point of view.

Noel Petty

Cinderella

Cinderella
Sat moping in the cellar.
There was no way at all
That she could get to the ball.

Kim Richardson

Macbeth

Macbeth
Was brave in the face of death.
But he wasn't quite as tough
As Macduff.

Kim Richardson

Colour poems

A colour poem is a poem in which a poet writes about what different colours remind them of or focuses on a single colour.

What is pink?

What is pink? A rose is pink
By the fountain's brink.
What is red? A poppy's red
In its barley bed.
What is blue? The sky is blue
Where the clouds float through.
What is white? A swan is white
Sailing in the light.
What is yellow? Pears are yellow,
Rich and ripe and mellow.
What is green? The grass is green,
With small flowers between.
What is violet? Clouds are violet
In the summer twilight.
What is orange? Why, an orange,
Just an orange!

Christina Rossetti

Colour Story – from Gold to Silver

Gold is a blaring trumpet call.
Blue is a shivering stream.
Yellow is a tickle of laughter.
White is the whistling dream.

Red is a scream, a strangled cry.
Orange is the spluttering flames.
Grey is the murmuring mist.
Silver is the rattle of chains.

John Foster

Symphony in Yellow

An omnibus across the bridge
    Crawls like a yellow butterfly,
    And, here and there, a passer-by
Shows like a little restless midge.

Big barges full of yellow hay
    Are moored against the shadowy wharf,
    And, like a yellow silken scarf,
The thick fog hangs along the quay.

The yellow leaves begin to fade
   And flutter from the Temple elms,
   And at my feet the pale green Thames
Lies like a rod of rippled jade.

Oscar Wilde

I Asked the Little Boy Who Cannot See

I asked the little boy who cannot see,
'And what is colour like?'
'Why, green,' said he,
'Is like the rustle when the wind blows through
The forest; running water, that is blue;
And red is like a trumpet sound; and pink
Is like the smell of roses; and I think
That purple must be like a thunderstorm;
And yellow is like something soft and warm;
And white is a pleasant stillness when you lie
And dream.'

Anon.

Airmail to a Dictionary

Black is the mellow night
Without the black there would be no night.

Black is the pupil of the eye
Putting colour in the sea's skin and earthen sky.

Black is the oil of the engine
On which this whole world is depending.

Black is light years of space
Holding on its little finger this human race.

Black is the colour of ink
That makes the History books we print.

Black is the army. Wars in the night
Putting on the black to hide the white.

Black is the colour of coal
Giving work to the miners and warmth to the cold.

Black is the strip upon my cardcash
That lets me get money from the Halifax.

Black is the shade of the tree
Sharp in definition against inequality.

Black is the eclipse of the sun
Displaying its power to everyone.

Black is the ink from a history
That shall redefine the dictionary.

Black on black is black is black is
Strong as asphalt and tarmac is.

Black is a word that I love to see
Black is that, yeah, black is me.

Lemn Sissay

Column poems

*A column poem is a poem in which the words are
presented in columns. In some cases, column poems consist
of two separate poems that are developed side by side in
order to provide a contrast.*

Wild Bear

Tame Bear

(Can it be the same bear?)

Bears in the bushes,
bears in the trees,
bears scoffing mice and frogs,
gobbling grass and leaves.

Bears fishing rivers,
bears killing seals,
bears on other bears
picking off fleas.

Bears in a circus,
bears wearing chains,
bears bearing blisters
dancing in pain.

Bears bored stiff in pits,
bears begging food,
bears biting other bears,
bleeding from wounds.

Gina Douthwaite

How Do I Feel?

How do I feel?
My face can't lie –

with furrowed brow
and narrowed eye

and zipped-up teeth
that want to bite,

you'll know I'm looking
for a fight.

How do I feel?
My face can't lie –

it's like the sun
up in the sky

with eyes like worms
bridged up to kiss,

I'm happy when
I look like this.

Gina Douthwaite

Column Poems

Column
poems
stretch
towards
the
sky
like
tall
grey
towers.

Column
poems
stretch
towards
the
sky
like
tall
green
trees.

Sean Forbes

This = That

A nice poem	An ice poem
You sing	Using
I sing	icing
sugar	sugar
ikon	I can
ice a	ice a
bun.	bun.

I sand	Ice and
milk or	milk, or
water	water-
I scan	ice can
make	make
I screams.	ice-creams.

Anon.

False Alarm

Flashes
illuminate
a sombre
sky
a crack
then roar
upon roar
fills
the air
before
a fusillade
of silver
bullets
is unleashed
shattering
the silence
of the trees.

My son
wakes up
with a
startled cry
Go back
to sleep
little one
No
the revolution
has not
begun
It's
only
the
beginning
of the
rainy season.

Cecil Rajendra

Concrete poems

A concrete poem is a type of poem in which the layout of a word or words is designed to represent a feature of the subject.

Spectacles

Andrew Collett

Tyrannosaurus Rex

Stanley Cook

C

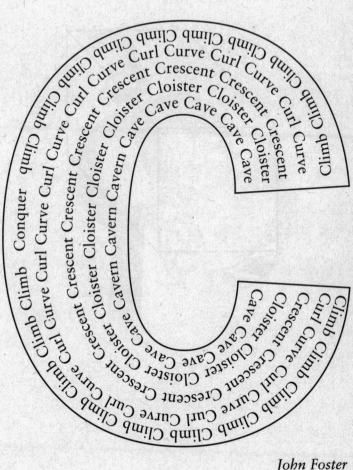

John Foster

ice cube

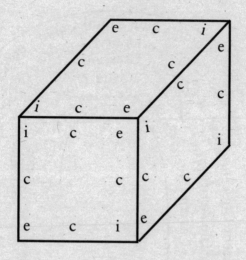

Derek Stuart

Conversation poems

A conversation poem is any poem which takes the form of a conversation.

What's Your Name?

What's your name?
Mary Jane.
Where do you live?
Cabbage Lane.
What's your number?
Rain and thunder.
What address?
Watercress.

What's your name?
Johnny Maclean.
Where do you live?
Down the lane.
What's your shop?
Lollipop.
What's your number?
Cucumber.

Anon.

Father William

'You are old, Father William,' the young man said,
  'And your hair has become very white;
And yet you incessantly stand on your head –
  Do you think, at your age, it is right?'

'In my youth,' Father William replied to his son,
  'I feared it might injure the brain;
But now that I'm perfectly sure I have none,
  Why I do it again and again.'

'You are old,' said the youth, 'as I mentioned before,
  And have grown most uncommonly fat;
Yet you turned a back somersault in at the door –
  Pray, what is the reason of that?'

'In my youth,' said the sage, as he shook his grey locks,
  'I kept all my limbs very supple
By the use of this ointment – one shilling the box –
  Allow me to sell you a couple.'

'You are old,' said the youth, 'and your jaws are too weak
  For anything tougher than suet;
Yet you finished the goose, with the bones and the beak –
  Pray, how did you manage to do it?'

'In my youth,' said his father, 'I took to the law,
   And argued each case with my wife;
And the muscular strength, which it gave to my jaw,
   Has lasted the rest of my life.'

'You are old,' said the youth, 'one would hardly suppose
   That your eye was as steady as ever;
Yet you balanced an eel on the end of your nose –
   What made you so awfully clever?'

'I have answered three questions and that is enough,'
   Said his father, 'don't give yourself airs!
Do you think I can listen all day to such stuff?
   Be off, or I'll kick you downstairs!'

Lewis Carroll

Two Traffic Wardens Talking on Christmas Eve

Nabbed any good ones yet?
Too right I have, a big fat geezer
with a white beard wearing a red suit
and he's only trying to park
some kind of open truck on a double yellow line.

So you says to him push off?
Too right I did, I says to him, 'Oi
what do you think you are playing at here, old son? Eh?
This is a restricted zone, you can't park that thing here
especially with those animals.'

Animals? What animals?
Horrible great big deer things with vicious horns
and he keeps laughing and saying, 'Ho Ho Ho.'
I says to him, 'You'll soon stop laughing
when I write out this parking ticket, old lad.'

Nice one, Stan, so what happened then?
One of those nasty great deer things
really ugly looking he was, with a shiny red hooter
only goes and eats my parking ticket
and tries to eat the rest of my pad as well as my hat.

Cheeky so and so, I hope you told him what for.
I did , I can tell you, I said, 'Oi! What's your game then?'
And he turns round and goes 'Ho Ho Ho' back at me
tells me he's some kind of van driver
with a load of kids' toys and stuff to deliver.

So what? A double yellow line's a double yellow line.
Exactly, I soon told him, silly old fool
Looked him straight in the eye and wrote out a ticket
on the back of a shopping list I had handy
'Who do you think you are?' I said. 'Father Christmas?'

David Harmer

'Mummy, Oh Mummy'

'Mummy, Oh Mummy, what's this pollution
That everyone's talking about?'
'Pollution's the mess that the country is in,
That we'd all be far better without.
It's factories belching their fumes in the air,
And the beaches all covered with tar,
Now throw all those sweet papers into the bushes
Before we get back in the car.'

'Mummy, Oh Mummy, who makes pollution,
And why don't they stop if it's bad?
''Cos people like that just don't think about others,
They don't think at all, I might add.
They spray all the crops and they poison the flowers,
And wipe out the birds and the bees,
Now there's a good place we could dump that old mattress
Right out of sight in the trees.'

'Mummy, Oh Mummy, what's going to happen
If all the pollution goes on?'
'Well the world will end up like a second-hand junk-yard,
With all of its treasures quite gone.
The fields will be littered with plastics and tins,
The streams will be covered with foam,
Now throw those two pop bottles over the hedge,
Save us from carting them home.'

'But Mummy, Oh Mummy, if I throw the bottles,
Won't that be polluting the wood?'
'Nonsense! That isn't the same thing at all,
You just shut up and be good.
If you're going to start getting silly ideas
I'm taking you home right away.
'Cos pollution is something that other folk do,
We're just enjoying our day.'

Anon.

Counting poems

A counting poem is a poem in which counting of some kind plays a significant part.

One Old Oxford Ox

One old Oxford ox opening oysters;
Two teetotums totally tired trying to trot to Tadbury;
Three tall tigers tippling tuppenny tea;
Four fine foxes fanning fainting friars;
Five flighty flibbertigibbets foolishly fishing for flies;
Six sportsmen shooting snipe;
Seven Severn salmon swallowing shrimp;
Eight Englishmen eagerly examining Europe;
Nine nimble noblemen nibbling noodles;
Ten tinkers tinkling upon ten tinderboxes with ten
    tenpenny tacks;
Eleven elephants elegantly equipped;
Twelve talkative tailors trimming tartan trousers.

Anon.

One Pink Sari

One pink sari for a pretty girl,
Two dancing women all in a whirl,
Three charmed cobras rising from a basket,
Four fat rubies in the rajah's casket,

Five water carriers straight and tall,
Six wicked vultures sitting on the wall,
Seven fierce tigers hiding in the grass,
Eight elephants rolling in a warm mud bath,
Nine green parrots in the coconut tree;
Ten twinkling stars, a-twinkling at me.

Anne Marie Linden

Crocodile One, Alligator Two

Crocodile one, alligator two
Who's been causing a hullabaloo?

Elephant three, rhinoceros four
Who's been banging on the kitchen door?

Monkey five, chimpanzee six
Who's been getting up to lots of tricks?

Penguin seven, walrus eight
Who's been swinging on the garden gate?

Kangaroo nine, donkey ten
Who's been getting up to mischief again?

John Foster

Back Track, Cycle Rack

(To the tune of Nick-Nack Paddywhack)

John ate one,
Sue ate two.
They ate picnics at the zoo.
With a lunch pack, haversack, the lion picnicked too,
First on John and then on Sue!

Lee climbed three,
Sean climbed four.
They hadn't climbed so high before.
With a chimneystack, steeplejack, never sneeze or cough,
But Lee did and blew Sean off!

Clive rode five,
Vic rode six.
Rode their bikes off to the sticks.
With a back track, cycle rack, never mind the cost.
Clive crashed his and Vic got lost!

Kevin won seven,
Kate won eight.
They won goldfish at the fete.
With a pac-a-mac, thunder clap, the rain came pouring
    down.
Kev's fish snorkelled, Kate's fish drowned!

Di rang nine,
Ben rang ten.
Rang up all their bestest friends.
With a joke crack, have a laugh, now it's time for fun.
Our rhyme's told, our song is sung.

Maureen Haselhurst

Dem Bones Gonna Rise Again!

In come de animals two by two:
Hippopotamus and a kangaroo;
   Dem bones gonna rise again!

In come de animals three by three:
Two big cats and a bumblebee;
   Dem bones gonna rise again!

In come de animals four by four:
Two through de window, and two through de door;
   Dem bones gonna rise again!

In come de animals five by five:
Almost dead and hardly alive;
   Dem bones gonna rise again!

In come de animals six by six:
Three wid cubs and three wid sticks;
   Dem bones gonna rise again!

In come de animals seven by seven:
Four from hell and de others from heaven;
  Dem bones gonna rise again!

In come de animals eight by eight:
Four on time, and de others late;
  Dem bones gonna rise again!

In come de animals nine by nine:
Four in front and five behin';
  Dem bones gonna rise again!

In come de animals ten by ten:
Five big roosters and five big hens;
  Dem bones gonna rise again!

Dem bones gonna rise again,
Dem bones gonna rise again,
I knows, Oh! I knows it shuah –
Dem bones gonna rise again!

Anon.

What Is One?

One is the sun,
a rhino's horn,
a drop of dew,
a lizard's tongue.

One is the world,
a lonely whale;
an elephant's trunk,
a monkey's tail.

One is an acorn,
one is a moon,
one is a forest
felled too soon.

Judith Nicholls

Fortunes

One for sorrow, two for joy,
Three for a kiss and four for a boy,
Five for silver, six for gold,
Seven for a secret never to be told,
Eight for a letter from over the sea,
Nine for a lover as true as can be.

Anon.

Minus the Fun!

From 50 take away . . .
- The Prime Minister's door!
- The letters in the alphabet!
- The wives of King Henry VIII!

Now add . . .
- A baker's dozen
- The second highest odd number under 20
- The eyes on a Cyclops!

Now divide by . . .
- The wise monkeys!
  Did you get it?
  (Unlucky!)

Ian Bland

Couplets

A couplet is a pair of consecutive lines which rhyme. Many rhyming poems are written in couplets.

Ladybird! Ladybird!

Ladybird! Ladybird! Fly away home,
Night is approaching and sunset has come:
The herons are flown to their trees by the Hall;
Felt, but unseen, the damp dewdrops fall.
This is the close of a still summer day;
Ladybird! Ladybird! Haste! fly away!

Emily Brontë

The Months of the Year

January brings the snow;
Makes the toes and fingers glow.

February brings the rain,
Thaws the frozen ponds again.

March brings breezes loud and shrill,
Stirs the dancing daffodil.

April brings the primrose sweet,
Scatters daisies at our feet.

May brings flocks of pretty lambs,
Skipping by their fleecy dams.

June brings tulips, lilies, roses;
Fills the children's hands with posies.

Hot July brings cooling showers,
Strawberries and gilly-flowers.

August brings the sheaves of corn,
Then the Harvest home is borne.

Warm September brings the fruit,
Sportsmen then begin to shoot.

Fresh October brings the pheasant;
Then to gather nuts is pleasant.

Dull November brings the blast,
Then the leaves are falling fast.

Chill December brings the sleet,
Blazing fire and Christmas treat.

Sara Coleridge

Dreams

Here we are all, day by day; by night we are hurled
By dreams, each one into a several world.

Robert Herrick

Happy Thoughts

The world is so full of a number of things,
I'm sure we should all be as happy as kings.

Robert Louis Stevenson

The Desired Swan-song

Swans sing before they die – 'twere no bad thing
Should certain persons die before they sing.

Samuel Taylor Coleridge

Lower the Diver

Lower the diver over the side
Down to the roots of the swirling tide.

Lower the diver, weighted with lead,
Glass and brass helmet over his head.

Lower the diver on to the deck
And the barnacled masts of the long-lost wreck.

Lower the diver; will he find jars,
Rust-sealed treasure chests, silver bars?

Lower the diver; will he find gold,
Cannon-balls, skulls, or an empty hold?

Lower the diver; pray that the shark
Doesn't mind guests in the salty dark.

Lower the diver; then man the winch,
Wind him up slowly, inch by inch.

Undo his helmet. Why does he weep?
Is it so bad to be hauled from the deep?

Talk to the diver. What does he mean –
'Mermaids are real and her eyes were green'?

Richard Edwards

Autumn Birds

The wild duck startles like a sudden thought,
And heron slows as if it might be caught;
The flopping crows on weary wings go by,
And greybeard jackdaws, noising as they fly;
The crowds of starlings whizz and hurry by
And darken like a cloud the evening sky;
The larks like thunder rise and suther round
Then drop and nest in the stubble ground;
The wild swan hurries high and noises loud,
With white necks peering to the evening cloud.
The weary rooks to distant woods are gone;
With length of tail the magpie winnows on
To neighbouring tree, and leaves the distant crow,
While small birds nestle in the hedge below.

John Clare

D is for . . .

Diamond poems

*A diamond poem is any poem in the shape of a diamond.
Often the shape is created by having a certain number of
syllables in each line.*

Two Diamond Poems

Spark
Glows red
In wind's breath.
Struggles for life.
Flickers. Dies. Flickers.
Bursts into flame.
Twists and leaps.
Dancing
Fire.

Hawk
Eyes bright
Scans the moor
For signs of prey
Pinpoints a target
Suddenly swoops
Claws ready:
Airborne
Death.

John Foster

Vowel Play

a	e	i	o	u
an	me	it	or	us
can	met	sit	ore	use
scan	meat	site	sore	used
scant	meant	spite	store	mused
cant	mean	spit	tore	muse
ant	men	pit	tor	use
an	me	it	or	us
a	e	i	o	u

Sean Forbes

The Pole Star

High
Above
The dark world
Shining brightly,
A pinpoint of light
Guiding sailors
Towards home –
The Pole
Star.

John Scotby

Diary poems

*A diary poem is one that is presented in the form of an
entry or series of entries in a diary.*

The Secret Diary of a Dragon

Monday
Polished my scales
till they shone like the sea.
Pity Ma won't let me paint my claws.
Tried trampling the ground –
it didn't look bad, but
I'm not too happy about my roars.

Tuesday
Measured my wings
on the door of the cave
still only a measly ten feet long.
I'm trying to master
that flick of the tail
that knocks a knight down, however strong.

Wednesday
Went out to practise
breathing fire;
not a success, I must admit.
Only managed one small puff of smoke –
I couldn't help feeling a bit of a twit.

Thursday
Spotted a knight
riding over the plain.
Looked small enough for me to attack.
I had some trouble taking off;
it got too dark – I had to come back.

Friday
I saw this maiden
wandering by.
Thought I'd try to carry her away.
But I couldn't endure
the way she screamed.
So I put it off for another day.

Sheila Simmons

Extract from a Reindeer's Diary

Boxing Day

Slept.

Erica Stewart

Football Training

Monday
Practised heading the ball:
Missed it – nutted the neighbours' wall.

Tuesday
Perfected my sideline throw:
Fell in the mud – forgot to let go!

Wednesday
Worked on my penalty kick:
A real bruiser – my toe met a brick.

Thursday
Gained stamina – went for a jog:
Ran round in circles – lost in the fog!

Friday
Developed my tactical play:
Tackled the goalpost – it got in the way.

Saturday
Exercised – twenty-eight press-ups:
Did pull a muscle – but no major mess-ups.

Sunday
At last – the day of the match!
Came through it all without a scratch.
The ref was amazed how I kept my nerve;
He agreed it's not easy to be the reserve!

Celia Warren

E is for . . .

Elegies

An elegy is a poem or song which is a lament for a person or an animal that has died.

from *Elegy Written in a Country Churchyard*

The curfew tolls the knell of parting day,
The lowing herd winds slowly o'er the lea,
The ploughman homeward plods his weary way,
And leaves the world to darkness and to me.

Now fades the glimmering landscape on the sight,
And all the air a solemn stillness holds,
Save where the beetle wheels his droning flight,
And drowsy tinklings lull the distant folds;

Save that from yonder ivy-mantled tow'r
The moping owl does to the moon complain
Of such as, wand'ring near her secret bow'r,
Molest her ancient solitary reign.

Beneath those rugged elms, that yew-tree's shade,
Where heaves the turf in many a mould'ring heap,
Each in his narrow cell for ever laid,
The rude forefathers of the hamlet sleep.

Thomas Gray

Lament for Thomas Macdonagh

He shall not hear the bittern cry
In the wild sky, where he is lain.
Nor voices of the sweeter birds
Above the wailing of the rain.

Nor shall he know when loud March blows
Thro' slanting snows her fanfare shrill,
Blowing to flame the golden cup
Of many an upset daffodil.

But when the Dark Cow leaves the moor,
And pastures poor with greedy weeds,
Perhaps he'll hear her low at morn
Lifting her horn in pleasant meads.

Francis Ledwidge

Elegy for a Much-loved Dog

How beautiful she was
With her amber eyes
Ears hemmed like silk purses
Their insides soft as the petals of iris
Her hound's high haunches
Her poor docked stump of a tail.

How afraid she was
Of the paper lampshades ghostly shifting
Of the dragon-fire of hot-air balloons
Of the vet's cold floor
Of being alone.

How comforting she was
With her welcoming skid down the stairs
Her grunts and snuffles in the creaky basket
Her jump and flump on the bed
The collapse of legs, the warm dump
Of herself, her dry biscuity smell,
Her contented 'Humph'.

How she could lift the heart
In exuberant take-off after a rabbit
How, for her, our going out
Into field or wood, was a going home.
How elegant her trot, her point,
Her pose on the seat in the window
How she was the book
Of the children's childhood.

How long her dying took.

Diana Hendry

Nine Lives

i.m. *Thisbe (1976–1990)*

This is my grave by the holly tree,
Remember me?

I am the cat who arrived by rail
Without a tail.

I am the cat who tried walking on water
Which would not support her.

I am the cat who got stuck on the ledge,
Too near the edge.

I am the cat who was locked in the shed
And could not be fed.

I am the cat who ran in the road
Where traffic flowed.

I am the cat who spat in the night
And lost the fight.

I am the cat who hid out in the snow
When you wanted to go.

I am the cat who with arthritic bones
Concealed her groans.

I am the cat who that autumn day
Just faded away.

This is my grave by the holly tree,
Remember me.

Sandy Brownjohn

Epigrams

An epigram is a short poem, especially one which has a witty and ingenious ending.

Epigram

Engraved on the Collar of a Dog which I Gave to His Royal Highness

I am his Highness' Dog at Kew;
Pray tell me, sir, whose dog are you?

Alexander Pope

Treason

Treason doth never prosper; what's the reason?
For if it prosper, none dare call it treason.

Anon.

Kings and Tyrants

'Twixt kings and tyrants there's this difference known,
Kings seek their subjects' good; tyrants their own.

Anon.

A Word Is Dead

A word is dead
When it is said,
Some say.
I say it just
Begins to live
That day.

Emily Dickinson

Epitaphs

An epitaph is a short piece of writing inscribed on a gravestone. Some epitaphs take the form of a verse.

Anonymous Epitaphs

Here lies a man who was killed by lightning;
He died when his prospects seemed to be brightening.
He might have cut a flash in this world of trouble,
But the flash cut him and he lies in the stubble.

Anon.

Owen Moore
Gone away
Owin' more
Than he could pay.

Anon.

Here lies a chump who got no gain
From jumping from a moving train.
Banana skins on platform seven
Ensured his terminus was Heaven.

Anon.

Nursery Epitaphs

Here lies the body
Of Contrary Mary,
Poisoned by milk
From the local dairy.

Here lies the body
Of Little Bo Peep,
Tramped to death
By a very large sheep.

Here lies the body
Of Little Miss Muffet,
Bitten by a spider
Hiding in her tuffet.

Here lies the body
Of Mr Toad,
Squashed by a lorry
On a very busy road.

John Kitching

Doctor Foster

Here lies the body
Of Doctor Foster,
Drowned in a puddle
On his way to Gloucester.

Evie Foster

from *Resting Pets*

Here lies our pet koala bear
Who feared the sound of thunder;
Out went his light in a storm one night
And now he's back down under.

Here lies a pet camel
So cold in the ground;
You can tell it's his grave
By the double mound.

Beneath this stone lie the flesh and bone
Of our cockatoo, Renato;
He died of the blight in the middle of the night
When he swallowed a green tomato.

Here lies Flossie
Our favourite pussy;
Frequently bossy,
Occasionally fussy;
Her grave is grassy,
Rather than mossy,
Cos mossy's not classy
Enough for Flossie.

Here lies the body of our dog Mac
Who once ran away and never came back.

Stranger, tread softly
Our budgie's gone west;
And somewhere round here
We laid her to rest.

Jack Ousbey

Byron's Dog, Boatswain

*The poet, Lord Byron, wrote this inscription on a
marble monument which he had erected in memory
of his favourite dog.*

NEAR THIS SPOT
ARE DEPOSITED THE REMAINS OF ONE
WHO POSSESSED BEAUTY WITHOUT VANITY,
STRENGTH WITHOUT INSOLENCE,

COURAGE WITHOUT FEROCITY,
AND ALL THE VIRTUES OF MAN WITHOUT HIS
  VICES.
THIS PRAISE, WHICH WOULD BE UNMEANING
FLATTERY IF INSCRIBED OVER HUMAN ASHES,
IS BUT A JUST TRIBUTE TO THE MEMORY OF
BOATSWAIN, A DOG,
WHO WAS BORN AT NEWFOUNDLAND, MAY 1803
AND DIED AT NEWSTEAD ABBEY, NOV 18, 1808.

Lord Byron

On a Tired Housewife

Here lies an old woman who was always tired,
She lived in a house where help wasn't hired:
Her last words on earth were: 'Dear friends, I am going
To where there's no cooking, or washing, or sewing,
For everything there is exact to my wishes,
For where they don't eat there's no washing of dishes.
I'll be where loud anthems will always be ringing,
But having no voice I'll be quit of the singing.
Don't mourn for me now, don't mourn for me never,
I am going to do nothing for ever and ever.

Anon.

F is for . . .

Fables

A fable is a poem which tells a story, especially with animals as characters, in order to convey a moral message.

The Mouse, the Frog and the Little Red Hen

Once a Mouse, a Frog and a Little Red Hen,
Together kept a house;
The Frog was the laziest of frogs
And lazier still was the Mouse.

The work all fell on the Little Red Hen,
Who had to get the wood,
And build the fires, and scrub and cook,
And sometimes hunt the food.

One day, as she went scratching round,
She found a bag of rye;
Said she, 'Now who will make some bread?'
Said the lazy Mouse, 'Not I.'

'Nor I,' croaked the Frog as he drowsed in the shade,
Red Hen made no reply,
But flew around with bowl and spoon,
And mixed and stirred the rye.

'Who'll make the fire to bake the bread?'
Said the Mouse again, 'Not I.'
And scarcely op'ning his sleepy eyes,
Frog made the same reply.

The Little Red Hen said never a word,
But a roaring fire she made;
And while the bread was baking brown,
'Who'll set the table?' she said.

'Not I,' said the sleepy Frog with a yawn;
'Nor I,' said the Mouse again.
So the table she set and the bread put on,
'Who'll eat this bread?' said the Hen.

'I will!' cried the Frog. 'And I!' squeaked the Mouse,
As they near the table drew:
'Oh, no you won't!' said the Little Red Hen,
And away with the loaf she flew.

Anon.

The Fox and the Crow

Now this is the story
of the fox who saw
a piece of cheese
on the forest floor.

And that fox he hopped
up and down with glee,
and he said,
'Oh my,
this cheese is for me!'

But before that fox
could blink his eyes,
a big black crow
came whizzing by,

And she took that cheese
up into a tree,
And the fox said,
'Man,
there goes my tea!'

But that fox was as sly
as a fox can be.
So he went
and stood
underneath the tree.

119

And he said,
'Oh my!
What a beautiful crow!
Your eyes they glisten,
they glint, they glow.

'Your feathers
all shine,
and your beak is sleek.
Oh, how I wish
I could hear you speak.

'Or better still,
I wish you'd sing.
For a bird like you
could sing for a king.

'Dear crow!
Sweet crow!
Oh, beautiful crow!
Please sing for me,
it would please me so.'

So the crow went
'CAW!'
and the fox he saw
that cheese fall down
to the forest floor.

'Oh no!'
said the crow.
'I've been taken in!'
'Quite right,'
said the fox
with a nasty grin.

And he ran
straight back
to his cosy den.
And the crow never fell
for that trick again!

Cynthia Rider

The Lion and the Echo

The King of the Beasts, deep in the wood,
Roared as loudly as it could.
Right away the echo came back
And the lion thought itself under attack.

'What voice is it that roars like mine?'
The echo replied, 'Mine, mine.'

'Who might you be?' asked the furious lion,
'I'm King of this jungle, this jungle is mine.'
And the echo came back a second time,
'This jungle is mine, is mine, is mine.'

The lion swore revenge if only it could
Discover the intruder in the wood.
It roared, 'Coward! Come out and show yourself!'
But the fearless echo replied simply '. . . elf.'

'Come out,' roared the lion, 'enough deceit,
Do you fear for your own defeat?'
But all the echo did was repeat
'Defeat . . . defeat . . .'

Frightened by every conceivable sound,
The exhausted lion sank to the ground.
A bird in a tree looked down and it said,
'Dear lion, I'm afraid that what you hear
Is simply the voice of your lion-sized fear.'

Brian Patten

G is for . . .

Greetings

A greetings poem is one that takes the form of a greeting of some kind.

A Greeting

Good morning, Life – and all
Things glad and beautiful.
My pockets nothing hold,
But he that owns the gold,
The Sun, is my great friend –
His spending has no end.

Hail to the morning sky,
Whose bright clouds measure high;
Hail to you birds whose throats
Would number leaves by notes;
Hail to you shady bowers,
And you green fields of flowers.

Hail to you women fair,
That make a show so rare
In cloth as white as milk –
Be't calico or silk:
Good morning, Life – and all
Things glad and beautiful.

W. H. Davies

A Celtic Greeting

May your garden grow good food
May your rain come clean
May your days stay fine
May your nights be silent
May your journeys bring your joy
And may all your litter go home with you.

Jane Whittle

Now Thrice Welcome, Christmas

Now thrice welcome, Christmas,
  Which brings us good cheer,
Minced pies and plum porridge,
  Good ale and strong beer;
With pig, goose and capon,
  The best that may be,
So well doth the weather
  And our stomachs agree.

Anon.

Farewell Old Year

Farewell old year,
With goodness crowned,
A hand divine hath set thy bound.

Welcome New Year,
Which shall bring
Fresh blessings
From Our Lord and King.

The old we leave without a tear,
The new we enter without fear.

Anon.

Dear March, Come In

Dear March, come in!
How glad I am!
I looked for you before.
Put down your hat –
You must have walked –
How out of breath you are!
Dear March, how are you?
And the rest?
Did you leave Nature well?
Oh, March, come right upstairs with me,
I have so much to tell!

I got your letter, and the birds' –
The maples never knew
That you were coming – I declare,
How red their faces grew!
But, March, forgive me –
And all those hills
You left for me to hue –
There was no purple suitable,
You took it all with you.

Who knocks? That April!
Lock the door!
I will not be pursued!
He stayed away a year, to call
When I am occupied.
But trifles look so trivial
As soon as you have come,
That blame is just as dear as praise
And praise as mere as blame.

Emily Dickinson

Good Morning, Parrots

Tell me,
how do you greet
A cockatoo and a parakeet?
Do you say
Good Day –
or How do you do,
To a Parakeet and a Cockatoo?

Do you say
Hello, *so* pleased to meet,
Mr Cockatoo and Miss Parakeet?

And when you go,
Do you say, Hello,
It's time to fly –
Or just, Good-bye,
Or Toodle-oo
Miss Parakeet,
Mr Cockatoo?

Anon.

H is for . . .

Haiku

A haiku is a traditional Japanese verse form, consisting of three lines which together add up to seventeen syllables. The first line has five syllables, the second line has seven syllables and the third line has five syllables.

Icy Morning Haiku

On a frozen pond
a small dog is nervously
attempting to skate

Way up in the tree
a black cat grins with delight
watching and waiting

Beneath the clear ice
a big fish wonders if all
dogs walk on water

James Carter

In the Stable: Christmas Haiku

Donkey
My long ears can hear
Angels singing, but my song
Would wake the baby.

Dog
I will not bark but
Lie, head on paws, eyes watching
All these visitors.

Cat
I'll wash my feet. For
This baby all should be clean.
My purr will soothe him.

Owl
My round eyes look down.
No starlit hunting this night:
Peace to little ones.

Spider
My fine web sparkles:
Indoor star in the roof's night
Over the baby.

Michael Harrison

Haiku Moments

1
Stems and leaves downy
hidden here white under stone,
to be green sunlight.

2
Ouch! tongue! lime juice knifed,
needled, scalded, bitten with
this charged sunlight sting!

3
Still *hot hot* fanning –
wish I stood barefoot in one
big field of new snow.

4
Mango – you sucked from
sunrise to sunset to be
this ripe scented flesh.

5
Settled in the bowl
alone, banana lies there
cuddle-curved, waiting.

James Berry

6 *shy haiku found hiding in the oaks in Parkin* Woods

twisting antler world –
dancing branches, swirling leaves
reaching for the sun

small village of ants
who carry moss, twigs, busy
paths lit by bluebells

alligator log
just lies there, green eyes watching,
waiting for dinner

midnight, silver bark
like strange white faces sleeping,
quiet moons lost in love

curvy branch like snake
slithers under dark green bush
– my mind disappears

in deep damp brown mud
worms play loud wiggle 'n' roll –
worm palace disco

Matt Black

I is for . . .

Insults

An insult poem is any poem that contains an insult or insults.

You!

You!
Your head is like a hollow drum.
You!
Your eyes are like balls of flame.
You!
Your ears are like fans for blowing fire.
You!
Your nostril is like a mouse's hole.
You!
Your mouth is like a lump of mud.
You!
Your hands are like drum-sticks.
You!
Your belly is like a pot of bad water.
You!
Your legs are like wooden posts.
You!
Your backside is like a mountain-top.

Traditional African

I'm Telling You

I'm as wise as an owl.
I'm as cunning as a cat.
You're as slimy as a snail.
You're as dirty as a rat.

I'm as brave as a lion.
I'm as strong as an ox.
You're as weak as a kitten.
You're as sneaky as a fox.

I'm as bright as a button.
I'm as hard as nails.
You're as useless as a yacht
Without any sails.

Sean Forbes

Beauty Spots

The rain makes all things beautiful,
The grass and flowers too.
If rain makes all things beautiful,
Why doesn't it rain on you?

Anon.

The Way to the Zoo

That's the way to the zoo.
That's the way to the zoo.
The monkey house is nearly full
But there's room enough for you.

Anon.

Thanks for the Photo

Thanks for the photo
It really was nice
I've put it in the attic
To scare away the mice.

Anon.

Roses Are Red

Roses are red
Grass is green
Your ears look cute
But there's nothing in between.

Anon.

You Remind Me of the Sea

'You remind me of the sea,' he said –
'Deep, untamed and wild.'
She sat there, looking modest,
Lovely, meek and mild.

'What a strange coincidence,'
She answered smooth and slick.
'You remind me of the sea as well –
You always make me sick . . .'

Clive Webster

You Are So Low

You are so low that, if there was a car on a bridge
and under the bridge there was a rock
and under the rock there was a stone
and under the stone there was a snail
and under the snail there was a bull ant
and under the bull ant there was a flea,
you could walk under the flea!

Anon.

Vocabulary for Villains

Fiendish, fearsome, filthy,
Revolting, rancid, vicious,
Detestable, disgusting,
Malevolent, malicious,

Ghastly, grisly, gruesome,
Menacing, atrocious,
Grim, grotesque, repulsive,
Loathsome, foul, ferocious,

Hellish, diabolical,
Hateful, hideous, mean,
Odious, malodorous,
Venomous, unclean,

Wicked, evil, ugly, vile,
Callous, cruel, spiteful,
Horrific, harsh, horrendous,
Pitiless and frightful.

I've given you the adjectives,
Now it's your turn to be clever:
Go ahead, enjoy it,
Write the vilest poem ever.

Eric Finney

Interviews

An interview poem is any poem that is presented in the form of an interview.

Interview with Mr Crabman, Superhero

May I sidle up to you
to ask a few questions?
>*Nothing too direct, please.*

Life cannot have been easy for you.
>*No, I had to claw my way to the top.*

You have a family.
>*A couple of nippers.*

You deal with specific crimes.
>*Mainly smash and crab.*

Do you stalk your prey?
>*These eyes were made for stalking.*

Tactics?
>*Pincer movements.*

How do you cope with injury?
>*I use crab sticks.*

How about transport?
>*I take a taxicrab.*

Do clients pay up?
>*Most shell up at once.*

Do you have any support?
>*Yes, we have an annual crab meet.*

What happens?
>*We play crabble*
>*and sing our song –*
>*'I did it sideways'.*

>John C. Desmond

The Poet Interviews an Electricity Pylon

Q. *Where do you live?*

A. I can live in the countryside where I cross fields and hills. I can also tower over towns and cities. In remote areas of Scotland or Wales, I clamber over our highest mountains or stretch across valleys and lakes, glens and lochs.

Q. *Are you known by any other name than 'pylon'?*

A. No, but from now on I wish to be known as 'Skelemettleton'.

Q. *OK Skelemettleton, are you afraid of high winds?*

A. Me! Afraid of high winds? Not in the least. I could grab any strength of wind with one hand and twist the life out of its silly little blowiness. Huh, wind – nothing but a huffy-puffy little baby-breath.

Q. *If you're not afraid of the wind, are you scared of the electricity that runs through you?*

A. Don't be daft! Electricity is my life-blood, it surges in my steel bones like lightning screaming through

charged cloud! Oh how I love electro! It's so
exciting!

Q. *So you're not afraid of wild weather or the dangers of
electricity, is there anything you are scared of?*

A. Em . . . well there's one thing. You promise not to
laugh?

Q. *OK. I promise not to laugh.*

A. Well I don't like it when lots of them brush up
against my metal legs. It tickles.

Q. *What tickles?*

A. A pickle of sheep tickle.

John Rice

J is for . . .

Joke poems

A joke poem is a humorous poem which tells a joke or a series of jokes.

Family Doctor

My grandpa thinks he's a cricket ball,
And, sometimes, he's a bat.
He went and told the Doctor
And the Doctor said, 'Howzat?'

My sister went to the Doctor's.
In front of the Doctor she sat.
She said, 'Doctor, I think I'm invisible!'
And the Doctor said, 'Who said that?'

My uncle went to the Doctor's.
'I'm a toadstool!' I heard him shout.
The Doctor said, 'You're a fun guy.
There's not mushroom for doubt!'

My brother went to the Doctor's.
He was feeling under the weather.
He said, 'I think I'm some curtains!'
She said, 'Pull yourself together!'

Ian Larmont

As the Witch Said to the Skeleton

WITCH: Come on out of that cupboard.
SKELETON: I can't. I haven't got the face to.

WITCH: Oh, come on. There's a dance down the road.
   Why don't you go?
SKELETON: I haven't got any body to go with.

WITCH: Don't you know anyone?
SKELETON: No, I haven't got a single ghoul-friend.

WITCH: Well, you needn't sound so sorry for yourself.
SKELETON: Well, I've lost my voice; among other things
   I haven't got a leg to stand on.

WITCH: I suppose you were trying to throw yourself off
   that cliff yesterday?
SKELETON: No, I hadn't got the guts.

WITCH: Scared, eh?
SKELETON: Me scared? You couldn't make me jump
   out of my skin if you tried.

WITCH: I don't know why I bother with you – you're just
   a bone-idle old bonehead.
SKELETON: That's right.

Anon.

And How's Business, Then?

Tailor Just sew-sew.
Electrician It's pretty light.
Farmer Mine is growing.
Dustman It's picking up.
Refrigerator salesman It's not so hot.
Astronomer It's looking up.
Lift operator It has its ups and downs.
Optician It's looking better.
Author Mine is all write!

Anon.

I'm Thor!

The thunder god went for a ride
Upon his favourite filly.
'I'm Thor,' he cried,
And the horse replied,
'You forgot your thaddle, thilly!'

Anon.

The Cow

The cow stood on the hillside,
Its skin as smooth as silk,
It slipped upon a cowslip
And sprained a pint of milk.

Anon.

Doctor Bell

Doctor Bell fell down the well
And broke his collar-bone.
Doctors should attend the sick
And leave the well alone.

Anon.

K is for . . .

Kennings

A kenning is a descriptive phrase, or compound word, which is used to name something instead of using a noun. Anglo-Saxon poets often used kennings in their poems. For example, a river is sometimes described as 'the swan-path' and an arrow as 'a battle-adder'. Sometimes a poem consists of a list of kennings.

Sun

Lightbringer
Joymaker
Nightchaser
Cloudshaker.

Foodgrower
Gloomfighter
Heatgiver
Moonlighter.

Sleepender
Icebreaker
Leafrouser
Plantwaker.

Skinbrowner
Nosepeeler
Feetwarmer
Hearthealer.

Steve Turner

River

boat-carrier
bank-lapper
home-provider
tree-reflector
leaf-catcher
field-wanderer
stone-smoother
fast-mover
gentle-stroller
sun-sparkler
sea-seeker

June Crebbin

Two Kennings

Wild howler
Night prowler
Free mealer
Chicken stealer
Earth liver
Fright giver
Rusty splasher
Hunted dasher
Fox

Blobby maybe
Jelly baby
Black wriggler
Comma squiggler
Legs growing
Tail going
Pond plopper
Land hopper
  Frog

Daphne Kitching

Steam Train

Funnelled monster
Rackety tracker
Hooting tooter
Clackety clacker

Snorting bull
Huffing puffer
Smoke belcher
Chugging chuffer

Hissing snake
Snickerty snicker
Track thunderer
Clickerty clicker.

Erica Stewart

L is for . . .

Letter poems

A letter poem is any poem written in the form of a letter.

Dear Headteacher

Dear Headteacher
I'm writing to say sorry about your window that was
    smashed
It wasn't me that did it, but someone from my class

I didn't kick the ball at all, I didn't really know
I didn't see the shot that took it through your new
    window . . .

I wasn't even playing, I just happened to be standing
I didn't have a clue where the ball would end up landing

I wasn't really looking, my eyes were closed instead
It wasn't my fault that the ball bounced off my head

If it hadn't hit my head it would just have hit the wall
But you're the one who told me to be standing there at all

Everybody laughed at the ricochet deflection,
Well, everyone but me when the football changed direction

Everyone said 'Smashing!' and 'Look what a beauty!'
But it wasn't my fault, I was just on playground duty.

Paul Cookson

Thank You (it's what I've always wanted)

Dear Auntie,
Thanks for the hand-knitted cloud.
It will come in useful on sunny days,
though the grey colour has left me feeling
a bit under the weather.

Dear Uncle,
I'm not too sure how to feed a star?
And it was difficult to sleep last night
(on account of the star being so bright).

Dear Grandma,
Wow! My very own river! What can I say?
I did try to fold it up in my cupboard, but it leaked
and Mum had to call a plumber.

Dear Cousin,
I am writing . . . to . . . thank . . . you . . . for . . .
the . . . mountain
(sorry, am . . . out of breath . . .
climbing over it . . . to get . . .
the pencil out of my . . . drawer).

Dear Grandad,
It was very thoughtful of you
to give me my own city.
It's what I've always wanted.
There is a slight problem though with
squeezing 11 million people
into my room (and I won't even
mention all the buildings!)
but nevertheless,
Thank you.

Andrew Fusek Peters

Bee, I'm expecting you!

Bee, I'm expecting you!
Was saying yesterday
To somebody you know
That you were due.

The frogs got home last week,
Are settled and at work,
Birds mostly back,
The clover warm and thick.

You'll get my letter by
The seventeenth: reply,
Or better, be with me.
    Yours,
        Fly.

Emily Dickinson

Letter to an Unknown Father

Dear Father,

I have never seen you.
I do not know your name.
I've no idea where you live
Or whose should be the blame.

I wonder what you look like?
Maybe you look like me?
When I look in morning mirrors
Is yours the face I see?

Will I ever get to know you
Before the clock runs down?
How I wonder as I wander
Through all the tired town.

Although I've never known you,
I miss you all the same.
I wonder if you're sad like me
At this broken family game?

I hope one day to meet you
Before our race is run.
I think of you just every day.

Your puzzled, loving son.

John Kitching

Limericks

A limerick is a five-line poem with a particular pattern.
Lines 1, 2 and 5 are the same length and have the same
rhythm. They also end with the same rhyme. Lines 3 and 4
are short lines, with the same length, rhythm and rhyme.
The limerick was first made popular by the nineteenth-
century poet Edward Lear.

There Was a Young Lady Whose Chin

There was a young lady whose chin
Resembled the point of a pin:
  So she had it made sharp
  And purchased a harp,
And played several tunes with her chin.

Edward Lear

The Young Lady of Wilts

There was a young lady of Wilts
Who walked up to Scotland on stilts.
  When they said it was shocking
  To show so much stocking,
She answered, 'Then what about kilts?'

Edward Lear

Anonymous Limericks

There was a young lady called Millicent
Who hated the perfume that Willie sent,
    So she sent it to Liz
    Who declared, 'What a swizz
It's that silly scent Willie sent Millicent!'

She frowned and called him Mr.
Because in sport he kr.
    And so, in spite,
    That very night
This Mr. kr. sr.

A sea-serpent saw a big tanker
Bit a hole in her side and then sank her.
    It swallowed the crew
    In a minute or two
And then picked its teeth with the anchor.

There was an old man of Blackheath
Who sat on his set of false teeth.
    Said he with a start,
    'Oh Lord, bless my heart!
I have bitten myself underneath.'

Anon.

Three Limericks

A daring young acrobat, Fritz,
did as his finale the splits.
  It raised a big laugh
  when he split right in half
and was carried away in two bits.

A foolish young girl called Sheree
went and stood under a tree,
  but thunder was crashing
  and lightning was flashing.
'Oops!' said her ghost. 'Silly me!'

A skinny old fellow called Prune
took off in a massive balloon,
  but discovered, too late,
  he was too light a weight
and soared all the way to the moon.

Marian Swinger

The Limerick

The limerick's lively to write
Five lines to it – all nice and tight.
    Two long ones, two trick
    Little short ones; then quick
As a flash here's the last one in sight.

Take the curious case of Tom Pettigrew
And Hetty, his sister. When Hettigrew
    As tall as a tree
    She came just to Tom's knee.
And did *Tom* keep on growing? You bettigrew.

Write a limerick now. Say there was
An old man of some place, what he does,
    Or perhaps what he doesn't,
    Or isn't or wasn't
Want help with it? Give me a buzz.

David McCord

List poems
A list poem is any poem which is developed in the form of a list.

Quiet Things

Hush! I'll show you quiet things –
moon and stars and a barn owl's wings
speckled moth on mottled sill
white mare standing paper-still
gap-toothed gravestones, hollow trees
flat-roofed fungus colonies
coins and bones long buried deep
hedgehog hunched in spiny sleep.

Sue Cowling

Shopping List for a Fireworks Display

One sharp, frosty night.
An inky-black midnight sky.
Several metres of safety barrier.
A circle of Catherine Wheels.
A bouquet of Crick-Crack Chrysthanthemums.
A hoppit of Jumping Jacks.
A cacophony of Crackling Thunderbursts.
A zoom of Flight Rockets.

A cloudburst of Golden Showers.
A brilliance of Roman Candles.
A boom of Quadblast Bangers.
A zigzag of Sing Birds.
A torrent of Silver Fountains.
A rainbow of Bursting Violets.
One match.
15 minutes of magic.
One million Oohs and Aahs.

Irene Yates

Mr Khan's Shop

is dark and beautiful.
There are parathas,

garam masala,
nan breads full of fruit.

There are bhajis, samosas, dhal,
garlic, ground cumin seeds.

Shiny emerald chillies
lie like incendiary bombs.

There are bhindi in sacks,
aloo to eat with hot puris

and mango pickle. There's
rice, yogurt,

cucumber and mint
– raita to cool the tongue.

Sometimes you see
where the shop darkens

Mr Khan, his wife
and their children

round the table.
The smells have come alive.

He serves me
poppadoms, smiles,

re-enters the dark.
Perhaps one day

he'll ask me to dine with them:
bhajis, samosa, pakoras,

coriander, dhal.
I'll give him this poem: *Sit down*

young man, he'll say
and eat your words.

Fred Sedgwick

In the Cave

When we went to explore
 the cave on the shore,
  here's what we found . . .

a rusty tin,
a bottle with a message in,
an old and crumpled treasure map,
a brass badge from a sailor's cap,
strips of canvas from a sail,
planks from a ship wrecked in a gale,
slimy seaweed, polished stones,
shiny shells and whitened bones.

In the cave that's what we found,
scattered on the sandy ground.

Sean Forbes

Pleasant Sounds

The rustling of leaves under the feet in woods and under
  hedges;
The crumping of cat-ice and snow down wood-rides,
  narrow lanes and every street causeway;
Rustling through a wood or rather rushing, while the wind
  halloos in the oak-top like thunder;

The rustle of birds' wings startled from their nests or flying
   unseen into the bushes;
The whizzing of larger birds overhead in a wood, such as
   crows, puddocks, buzzards;
The trample of robins and woodlarks on the brown leaves,
   and the patter of squirrels on the green moss;
The fall of an acorn on the ground, the pattering of nuts
   on the hazel branches as they fall from ripeness;
The flirt of the groundlark's wing from the stubbles – how
   sweet such pictures on dewy mornings, when the dew
   flashes from its brown feathers.

John Clare

To Every Thing There Is a Season

To every thing there is a season
and a time to every purpose under the heaven;
A time to be born, and a time to die; a time to plant,
and a time to pluck up that which is planted;
A time to kill, and a time to heal;
a time to break down, and a time to build up;
A time to weep, and a time to laugh;
a time to mourn, and a time to dance;
A time to cast away stones, and a time to gather
stones together; a time to embrace, and a time
to refrain from embracing;
A time to get, and a time to lose;

a time to keep, and a time to cast away;
A time to rend, and a time to sew;
a time to keep silence, and a time to speak;
A time to love, and a time to hate;
a time of war, and a time of peace.

from *The Bible (Ecclesiastes, Chapter 3, Verses 1–8)*

Lullabies

A lullaby is a song used to help lull a baby to sleep.

Sweet and Low

Sweet and low, sweet and low,
Wind of the western sea,
Low, low, breathe and blow,
Wind of the western sea,
Over the rolling waters go,
Come from the dying moon and blow,
Blow him again to me,
While my little one, while my pretty one, sleeps.

Alfred, Lord Tennyson

Now the Day Is Over

Now the day is over,
Night is drawing nigh,
Shadows of the evening,
Steal across the sky.

Now the darkness gathers,
Stars begin to peep,
Birds and beasts and flowers,
Soon will be asleep.

Sabine Baring-Gould

Holy Lullaby

Sleep, baby, sleep.
Thy father guards the sheep;
Thy mother shakes the dreamland tree,
Down falls a little dream for thee:
Sleep, baby, sleep.

Sleep, baby, sleep.
The large stars are the sheep;
The little stars are lambs, I guess;
And the gentle moon is the shepherdess:
Sleep, baby, sleep.

Sleep, baby, sleep.
Our Saviour loves His sheep;
He is the Lamb of God on high,
Who for our sakes came down to die:
Sleep, baby, sleep.

Anon.

Drift Upon a Dream

Hear the moon's whisper
as it slips across the sky.
Listen to the stars sing
their distant lullaby.
Feel the night wind's breath
– a faint brush upon your cheek.
Drift upon a rainbow's dream
and gently fall asleep.

John Foster

African Lullaby

Sleep, my little one!
The night is all wind and rain.
The meal has been wet by the raindrops
And bent is the sugarcane.

O Giver who gives to the people
In safety my little son keep!
My little son with head-dress,
Sleep, sleep, sleep!

Traditional African

Sandmen, Sandmen

Sandmen, sandmen,
  Wise and creepy,
Croon dream songs
  To make us sleepy.

A lovely maid with deep dark eyes
Is queen of all their lullabies.
On her ancient moon-guitar
She strums a sleep-song to a star;
And when the deep dark shadows fall
Snow-white lilies hear her call.

  Sandmen, sandmen,
    Wise and creepy,
  Croon dream songs
    To make us sleepy.

Anon.

A Cradle Song

Golden slumbers kiss your eyes,
Smiles awake you when you rise.
Sleep, pretty wantons, do not cry,
And I will sing a lullaby:
Rock them, rock them, lullaby.

Care is heavy, therefore sleep you;
You are care, and care must keep you.
Sleep, pretty wantons, do not cry,
And I will sing a lullaby:
Rock them, rock them, lullaby.

Thomas Dekker

M is for . . .

Metaphor poems

A metaphor is a way of describing something or someone as though it were something else, in order to put a picture or an idea into a reader's mind through the comparison it makes. A metaphor poem is one which consists of a single extended metaphor or a series of metaphors.

The Night Is a Big Black Cat

The night is a big black cat
The Moon is her topaz eye,
The stars are the mice she hunts at night
In the field of the sultry sky.

G. Orr Clark

Gorse

Gorse is a trumpet song.
It spikes out of the earth,
A welcome pain.

It will spear your hands.
It will wound your skin,
Bead you with scarlet.

183

It is 'I am' in all seasons.
　It blares its trumpet song
　　Tan-ta-ra to the skies.

It is a still fire.
　Yellow on the hillsides,
　　Coldly burning.

Gerard Benson

Autumn Treasure

Autumn is a rich tycoon
counting in the treasure
from earth and seed invested
in every kind of weather.
Profits have grown steadily
in all the sun and rain
yielding berries, fruit and nuts
and bags of golden grain.

Lois Rock

Rainbows

A rainbow is a painted smile
  turned upside down.
It's a multi-coloured bridge
  spanning the streets of town.

A rainbow is a brilliant band
  across my sister's hair.
It's a fluorescent mountain
  piercing the morning air.

A rainbow is a skipping rope
  for our playground game.
It's a splash of coloured ink
  lighting the sky with flame.

A rainbow is a promise
  made before time grew old.
It's a mysterious magic place
  hiding a pot of gold.

Moira Andrew

The Sea

The sea is a battering ram
Carving caves from the cliff's face,
Hammering with fury,
Chipping away at the rock
As it pounds relentlessly
Back and forth, back and forth,
Till the cliff cracks.
Then, as if weary,
It withdraws for a while
And sits offshore,
Replenishing its strength,
Before hurtling in,
Foaming and hissing,
To strike again
With renewed venom.

John Foster

N is for . . .

Nonsense poems

A nonsense poem is a poem which describes nonsensical people, events or things or which uses nonsense words.

The Num-Num Bird

Have you ever heard of the Num-Num bird?
Have you ogled his terrible beak?
He could peck off your nose, or your fingers or toes,
With one speedy but effortless tweak.

The Num-Num nests in warm woolly vests
Which he steals from your washing line
And he uses the pegs to hold in his eggs
Of which he has eight or nine.

The Num-Num bird is a trifle absurd
For his legs are a metre long
And he speeds down the street with his size 12 feet
A-singing his Num-Num song.

If you ever hear a strange whisper in your ear
'Num-Num!' then you'd better run
For you're doomed if he sees your extremities
Cos he'll nibble them one by one.

Doda Smith

YUMMY!

Yaks like yoghurt!
Yes they do!
If a yak gets a yoghurt he yells
YABADABADOO!
If you give a yak a yoghurt
He will yell **YIPPEE!**
'Yoghurt is yummy
More yoghurt for me!'

Snakes like a snack of sausages
Sssssso they sssay
If a snake has a sausage
he will suck it all day.
So get a sizzling sausage
slap it on a slab
so every passing python says
'You are SSSSSsssimply FAB!'

Michaela Morgan

Ladies and Jellybeans

Ladies and jellybeans,
Reptiles and crocodiles
I stand before you
And sit behind you

To tell you something
I know nothing about.
There will be a meeting tomorrow night
Right after breakfast
To decide which colour
To whitewash the church.
There is no admission;
Just pay at the door.
There will be plenty of seats,
So sit on the floor.

Anon.

The Owl and the Pussy Cat

The Owl and the Pussy Cat went to sea
   In a beautiful pea-green boat,
They took some honey, and plenty of money,
   Wrapped up in a five-pound note.
The Owl looked up to the stars above,
   And sang to a small guitar,
'O lovely Pussy! O Pussy, my love,
   What a beautiful Pussy you are,
      You are,
      You are!
   What a beautiful Pussy, you are!'

Pussy said to the Owl, 'You elegant fowl!
    How charmingly sweet you sing!
O let us be married! too long we have tarried:
    But what shall we do for a ring?'
They sailed away for a year and a day,
    To the land where the Bong-tree grows,
And there in a wood a Piggy-wig stood,
    With a ring at the end of his nose,
        His nose,
        His nose,
    With a ring at the end of his nose.

'Dear Pig, are you willing to sell for one shilling
    Your ring?' Said the Piggy, 'I will.'
So they took it away, and were married next day
    By the Turkey who lives on the hill.
They dined on mince, and slices of quince,
    Which they ate with a runcible spoon;
And hand in hand, on the edge of the sand,
    They danced by the light of the moon,
        The moon,
        The moon,
    They danced by the light of the moon.

Edward Lear

Jabberwocky

'Twas brillig, and the slithy toves
Did gyre and gimble in the wabe;
All mimsy were the borogoves
And the mome raths outgrabe.

'Beware the Jabberwock, my son!
The jaws that bite, the claws that catch!
Beware the Jubjub bird and shun
The frumious Bandersnatch!'

He took his vorpal sword in hand:
Long time the manxome foe he sought –
So rested he by the Tumtum tree,
And stood awhile in thought.

And as in uffish thought he stood,
The Jabberwock, with eyes of flame,
Came whiffling through the tulgey wood,
And burbled as it came!

One two! One two! and through and through
The vorpal blade went snicker-snack!
He left it dead, and with its head
He went galumphing back.

'And hast thou slain the Jabberwock!
Come to my arms, my beamish boy!
O frabjous day! Callooh! Callay!'
He chortled in his joy.

'Twas brillig, and the slithy toves
Did gyre and gimble in the wabe;
All mimsy were the borogoves
And the mome raths outgrabe.

Lewis Carroll

Alien Love Poems

1
Ribblerabbles are red
Vorglesmoogs are blue
Borglemilk is sweet
And so are you

2
I love your lips like yellow jelly
Your eyes, that stick out from your belly
I love the way your nose inflates
I love your ears, like vuckle plates

(The ribblerabble is a small crimson bird that lives on the back of the vorglesmoog. The vorglemsoog is a big blue animal, like a bison but much hairier. The borgle is a small cow that lives in the tops of wassik trees. Vuckle plates are like dinner plates but much bigger, with lots of small holes to let vuckle juices drain away.)

Translated by Roger Stevens

O is for . . .

Odes

An ode is a type of lyric poem usually addressed to the subject.

To a Skylark

Hail to thee, blithe Spirit!
Bird thou never wert,
That from heaven, or near it,
Pourest thy full heart
In profuse strains of unpremeditated art.

Higher still and higher
From the earth thou springest
Like a cloud of fire;
The blue deep thou wingest,
And singing still doth soar, and soaring ever singest.

Percy Bysshe Shelley

To a Butterfly

I've watched you now a full half-hour,
Self-poised upon that yellow flower;
And, little Butterfly! Indeed
I know not if you sleep or feed.
How motionless! – not frozen seas
More motionless! And then
What joy awaits you, when the breeze
Hath found you out among the trees,
And calls you forth again!

This plot of orchard-ground is ours;
My trees they are, my Sister's flowers.
Here rest your wings when they are weary;
Here lodge as in a sanctuary!
Come often to us, fear no wrong;
Sit near us on the bough!
We'll talk of sunshine and of song,
And summer days when we were young;
Sweet childish days, that were as long
As twenty days are now.

William Wordsworth

Ode on Solitude

Happy the man whose wish and care
  A few paternal acres bound,
Content to breathe his native air
    In his own ground.

Whose herds with milk, whose fields with bread,
  Whose flocks supply him with attire;
Whose trees in summer yield him shade,
    In winter fire.

Blest, who can unconcern'dly find
  Hours, days and years slide soft away;
In health of body, peace of mind,
    Quiet by day.

Sound sleep by night, study and ease,
  Together mixt, sweet recreation;
And innocence, which most doth please
    With meditation.

Thus let me live, unseen, unknown;
  Thus, unlamented, let me die,
Steal from the world, and not a stone
    Tell where I lie.

Alexander Pope

P is for . . .

Parodies

A parody is a poem which imitates the style of another poem, e.g. by emphasizing particular aspects of the language or form of the original poem. A parody can be used not only to entertain but to make a serious point.

Harvest Hymn

We plough the fields and scatter
our pesticides again:
our seeds are fed and watered
by gentle acid rain.
We spray the corn in winter
till pests and weeds are dead –
who minds a little poison
inside his daily bread?

All good gifts around us
beneath our ozone layer
are safe, oh Lord,
so thank you Lord
that we know how to care.

Judith Nicholls

The Holly and the Ivy

The holly and the ivy,
One's prickly and one's not,
I sat down on the prickly one
And in the air I shot,

And shot up through the ceiling,
And shot up in the sky.
And wished a 'Merry Christmas' to
The pigeons passing by.

I shot above the rainbow,
And climbing towards heaven,
I wished a 'Merry Christmas' to
A Boeing 747.

I kept shooting higher
And higher, and soon
I was wishing 'Merry Christmas' to
The man in the moon.

Then I started to tumble
To fall back to earth,
To slow me down, I flapped my arms
For all that I was worth.

I fell back through the ceiling
And landed on a chair,
But luckily on a different one,
And the holly was not there.

So just you be careful
When Christmas comes round –
Be sure to check beneath you when
You're starting to sit down.

And just you remember
The thing I forgot:
The holly and the ivy –
One's prickly, one's not.

Richard Edwards

Alternative Nursery Rhymes

Hush-a-bye baby

Hush-a-bye baby
Your milk's in the tin
Mummy has got you
A nice sitter-in.

Hush-a-bye baby
Now don't give a frown
While Mummy and Daddy
Are out on the town.

Anon.

Twinkle twinkle chocolate bar

Twinkle twinkle chocolate bar
Your dad drives a rusty car
Press the starter
Pull the choke
Off he goes in a cloud of smoke.

Anon.

208

Humpty Dumpty

Humpty Dumpty sat on a chair
Eating black bananas
And where do you think he put the skins?
Down the king's pyjamas!

Anon.

Mary had a little lamb

Mary had a little lamb,
A lobster and some prunes,
A glass of milk, a piece of pie
And then some macaroons.

It made the busy waiters grin
To see her order so,
And when they carried Mary out
Her face was white as snow.

Anon.

Postcard poems

A postcard poem is a poem which is written in the form of a message on a postcard.

Postcard from School Camp

*D*ear Mum and Dad,
   Weather's poor, food's bad, teachers are grumpy,
Instructors are mad. Cramped in tent, cold at night, no dry
Clothes, boots too tight. Didn't like canoeing, hiking was
Tough, all in all I've had enough.

> Bye for now, may see you soon,
> If I survive this afternoon.
> Your loving son.
> Charlie xx

PS Can I come again next year?

Richard Caley

Postcards in 23 words

Postcard from Fairyland

Spell-binding scenery.
Lots of moonbathing,
(no tan).
Food delicious,
portions small.
Elves quarrelsome.
Was granted three wishes –
messed it up.
So home Thursday.

Postcard from Anywhere

I lie in bed
quite without fear,
play in the sand,
swim by the pier.
Having a wonderful time.
Glad you're not here.

Postcard from Three-Bear Cottage

Not much of a holiday.
The furniture is broken.
Daddy Bear booms all the time –
Baby Bear squeaks.
Nothing to eat but porridge.

Postcard from the North Pole

Surrounded by icy whiteness.
It's winter, and it's always night.
The stars twinkle forever.
But I miss you all –
and home –
and sunlight.

Gerard Benson

Postcard from the Garden Shed

Dear All,
I sit inside the garden shed
I have lots of food so I'm well fed,
I have a kettle to make my tea
And a blanket to put over me.
I have a chair so I can rest
And a friendly spider – a hairy pest.
I can play my music as loud as I like,
I can fiddle around with my bike.
I can make a mess and not clear it away
And I can't hear the arguing when you play.
I love you all, I know you love me,
But my shed provides some therapy!
Love Dad X

Coral Rumble

Poster poems

A poster poem is a poem written in the form of a poster.

A MESSAGE
FROM A LONG-SERVING MEMBER
OF THE BROWN PARTY

Vote for me
Your friendly earthworm,
Conservationist
Born and bred.
When I take your soil
I'll always give
Something better back instead.
I'm into things organic
And really most concerned
That you cast your vote
To ensure
The earthworm
Is returned.

Pat Moon

Song Thrush Poster

WORM SHORTAGE
due to hard ground.
There are
SNAIL-BASHING LESSONS
today at the rockery.
Learn how to spot
poisoned slugs
and snails!
6 a.m. prompt.
PLEASE WATCH OUT
FOR CATS!

Sue Cowling

This Is a Troll-bridge

This is a troll-bridge.
Cross it if you dare.
This is a troll-bridge.
Beware! Beware!

The trolls are waiting,
Lurking in their lair.
This is a troll-bridge.
Please take care!

Eileen Pickersgill

214

Prayers

A prayer poem is a poem written in the form of a prayer.

The Easterner's Prayer

I pray the prayer the Easterners do –
May the peace of Allah abide with you!
Wherever you stay, wherever you go
May the beautiful palms of Allah grow,
Through days of labour and nights of rest,
The love of good Allah make you blest.
So I touch my heart as Easterners do –
May the peace of Allah abide with you!

Salaam alaikum
(Peace be unto you)

Anon.

Prayer for Peace

Lord, make me a channel of Thy peace
that where there is hatred, I may bring love;
that where there is wrong, I may bring the spirit of
    forgiveness;
that where there is discord, I may bring harmony;
that where there is error, I may bring truth;
that where there is doubt, I may bring faith;
that where there is despair, I may bring hope;
that where there are shadows, I may bring light;
that where there is sadness, I may bring joy.

St Francis of Assisi

Grace at Kirkcudbright

Some have meat and cannot eat,
Some cannot eat that want it;
But we have meat and we can eat,
Sae let the Lord be thankit.

Robert Burns

Spring Prayer

For flowers that bloom about our feet;
For tender grass, so fresh, so sweet;
For song of bird and hum of bee;
For all things fair we hear or see,
Father in heaven, we thank Thee!

For blue of stream and blue of sky;
For pleasant shade of branches high;
For fragrant air and cooling breeze;
For beauty of the blooming trees,
Father in heaven, we thank Thee!

Ralph W. Emerson

The Prayer of the Tree

You who pass by and would raise your hand against me,
   hearken ere you harm me.
I am the heat of your hearth on the cold winter night, the
   friendly shade screening you from summer sun.
And my fruits are refreshing draughts quenching your
   thirst as you journey on.
I am the beam that holds your house, the board of your
   table, the bed on which you lie, the timber that builds
   your boat.
I am the handle of your hoe, the door of your homestead,

the wood of your cradle, the shell of your last resting
place.
I am the gift of God and the friend of man.
You who pass by, listen to my prayer and Harm me not.

Anon.

Prayer of a Fisherman

Lord let me catch a fish
So large that even I,
In telling of it afterwards,
Shall have no need to lie.

Anon.

A Student's Prayer

Now I lay me down to rest,
I pray I pass tomorrow's test.
If I should die before I wake
That's one less test I'll have to take.

Anon.

Give Thanks

Thanks for my eyes
Which give me sight
Of colour, shape and form,
The sunset in the evening,
The brilliance of the morn.

Thanks for my ears
Which give me sounds
Of laughter, music, talk.
The waves upon the sea-shore,
Leaves rustle as I walk.

Thanks for my nose
Which gives me scents
Of new-mown grass and rain.
The bacon sizzling in the pan,
The flowers in the lane.

Thanks for my mouth
Which gives me taste
Of all things sour and sweet.
Of apple pie and ice cream,
Delicious things to eat.

Thanks for my hands
Which give me touch
Of roughness or of smooth.
Of coldest snow or warmest sands
And gentle strokes to soothe.

But most of all
My sense of me
Of who I am, and want to be.
For loving thoughts and caring acts,
I give my thanks for me!

Brenda Williams

Mother's Day Prayer

Dear God
Today is Mother's Day
Please make her backache go away

May her pot plants grow all healthy
And a lottery win make her wealthy

May our dad buy her some flowers
And take us all to Alton Towers

May her fruitcake always rise
And the sun shine bright
In her blue skies

Roger Stevens

Puns

A pun is a play on words. Some wordplay poems are based on puns, using words with similar sounds but different meanings to create humour.

Copped

The policeman was all bleary-eyed
From getting out of bed,
He fumbled with his razor,
The shaving foam turned red –
He winced into the mirror,
'You're nicked,' the policeman said.

Richard Edwards

Punishment

An orange instead of an egg –
That's what the brown hen made!
And the chick's astonished comment was:
'Look what marmalade!'

Got this smashing new
Continental quilt
In stripes of pink and grey,
And now sheets, blankets,
Eiderdowns
Don't seem necessary
Duvet?

You may think I'm
Joking
When I tell you
I'm buying
'Lord of the Rings'
With my
Book Tolkien.

We've got this sauce competition
Going in our family:
I'm halfway down the salad cream,
Dad's nearly finished his H.P.
Mum, though, has only just started
Her favourite sauce:
It's up tomato ketchup, of course.

Eric Finney

Last Night

The Eskimo sleeps on his white bearskin,
And sleeps rather well I'm told.
Last night I slept in my little bare skin
And caught a terrible cold.

Anon.

Raising Frogs for Profit

Raising frogs for profit
Is a very sorry joke.
How can you make money
When so many of them croak?

Anon.

Seasick

'I don't feel whelk,' whaled the squid sole-fully.
'What's up?' asked the doctopus.
'I've got sore mussels and a tunny-hake,' she told him.

'Lie down and I'll egg salmon you,' mermaid the doctopus.
'Rays your voice,' said the squid. 'I'm a bit hard of
   herring.'
'Sorry! I didn't do it on porpoise,' replied the doctopus orc-
   wardly.

He helped her to oyster self on to his couch
And asked her to look up so that he could sea urchin.
He soon flounder a plaice that hurt.

'This'll make it eel,' he said, whiting a prescription.
'So I won't need to see the sturgeon?' she asked.
'Oh, no,' he told her. 'In a couple of dace you'll feel brill.'

'Cod bless you,' she said.
'That'll be sick squid,' replied the doctopus.

Nick Toczek

Q is for . . .

Question poems

A question poem is a poem that consists of a question or a series of questions with or without answers.

Morning

Will there really be a morning?
　　Is there such a thing as day?
Could I see it from the mountains
　　If I were as tall as they?
Has it feet like water lilies?
　　Has it feathers like a bird?
Is it brought from famous countries
　　Of which I've never heard?
Oh, some scholar! Oh, some sailor!
　　Oh, some wise man from the skies!
Please to tell a little pilgrim
　　Where the place called morning lies!

Emily Dickinson

O Dandelion

'O dandelion, yellow as gold,
What do you do all day?'

'I just wait here in the tall green grass
Till the children come to play.'

'O dandelion, yellow as gold,
What do you do all night?'

'I wait and wait till the cool dews fall
And my hair grows long and white.'

'And what do you do when your hair is white
And the children come to play?'

'They take me up in their dimpled hands
And blow my hair away.'

Anon.

Puzzle

It has always been a puzzle to me
What sailors sow when they 'plough' the sea.
What was it that made the window 'blind'?
Whose picture is put in a 'frame of mind'?
When a storm is 'brewing' what does it brew?
Does the 'foot' of a mountain wear a shoe?
Can a drink be got from a 'tap' at the door?
Does the 'edge' of the water cut the shore?
How long does it take to 'hatch' a plot?
Has a 'school' of herring a tutor or not?
Have you ever penned a 'volume' of smoke?
Can butter be made from the 'cream' of a joke?
Who is it fixes the 'teeth' in a gale?
To a king who 'reigns' why shout 'O Hail'?
Can you fasten the door with a 'lock' of hair?
Did a 'biting' wind ever bite you, and where?
Who is it paints the 'signs' of the times?
Does the moon change her 'quarters' for nickels and
    dimes?
What tune do you 'play' on your feelings, pray?
And who is it mends the 'break' of day?
And say – I'll admit this is quite absurd –
When you 'drop' a remark, do you 'break' your word?

Anon.

229

'Mother, May I Take a Swim?'

'Mother, may I take a swim?'
'Yes, my darling daughter,
But hang your clothes on a hickory limb
And don't go near the water.'

Anon.

A Ragman's Puzzle

Why is a foal like a loaf?
Why is an atom like a moat?
Why is a grin like a ring?
Why is toast like a stoat?

Why is a plum like a lump?
Why is a pager like a grape?
Why is a shrub like a brush?
Why is peat like a tape?

Why are gates like a stage?
Why is a leap like a plea?
Why is a café like a face?
Why is a leaf like a flea?

John Foster

Do Your Ears Hang Low?

Do your ears hang low?
Do they wobble to and fro?
Can you tie them in a knot?
Can you tie them in a bow?
Can you toss them over your shoulder
Like a regimental soldier?
Do your ears hang low?

Anon.

Answer Me This

When a great tree falls
And people aren't near,
Does it make a noise
If no one can hear?

And which came first
The hen or the egg?
The impractical question
We ask then beg.

Some wise men say
It's beyond their ken.
Did anyone ever
Ask the hen?

Anon.

The Man in the Wilderness

The Man in the Wilderness asked of me
'How many blackberries grow in the sea?'
I answered him as I thought good,
'As many red herrings as grow in the wood.'

The Man in the Wilderness asked me why
His hen could swim, and his pig could fly.
I answered him briskly as I thought best,
'Because they were born in a cuckoo's nest.'

The Man in the Wilderness asked me to tell
The sands in the sea and I counted them well.
Says he with a grin, 'And not one more?'
I answered him bravely, 'You go and make sure!'

Anon.

Uphill

Does the road wind uphill all the way?
    Yes, to the very end.
Will the day's journey take the whole long day?
    From morn to night, my friend.

But is there for the night a resting-place?
    A roof for when the slow, dark hours begin.
May not the darkness hide it from my face?
    You cannot miss that inn.

232

Shall I meet other wayfarers at night?
   Those who have gone before.
Then must I knock, or call when just in sight?
   They will not keep you standing at that door.

Shall I find comfort, travel-sore and weak?
   Of labour you shall find the sum.
Will there be beds for me and all who seek?
   Yea, beds for all who come.

Christina Rossetti

R is for . . .

Raps

A rap poem has a strong rhythmic beat and is often spoken to music. Raps are written to be spoken and performed, so the language of raps contains lots of words and phrases that are common in speech.

This Poem Has Class

This poem has class.
This poem has style.
This poem's in front
By more than a mile.

Easy come, easy go.
This is the poem
That will steal the show.

This poem's got rhythm.
This poem's got rhyme.
This poem knows
How to have a good time.

Take it fast, take it slow.
This is the poem
That will steal the show.

Put your hands together.
Let's hear you clap
The tip-top poem
That knows how to rap.

John Foster

The Palace Rap

There once was a queen
as proud as can be.
She was filled to the brim
with dignity.

Until a drummer
from a distant land
came to play
in the royal band.

And he played with a pitter
and a pit-pit-pat.
And he played with a rappety
rat-tat-tat.

And the queen she heard
in the drum's wild beat,
something that made her
tap her feet.

238

And her feet went a-tapping
and her hands went a-clapping,
and she said,
'I'm the queen
who's going to go a-rapping.'

So she rapped with a pitter
and a pit-pit-pat.
And she rapped with a rappety
rat-tat-tat.

She rapped round the ballroom.
She rapped round the throne.
But she didn't
like a-rapping
all on her own.

So the pageboy,
the footman,
the cook and the maid,
rapped around the palace
all that day.

And they rapped
out into
the palace yard
just in time for
the Changing of the Guard.

And the soldiers
threw their caps
in the air,
and they rapped up and down
Trafalgar Square.

And the tourists,
the shoppers,
and the city folk, too,
all said, 'What fun,
let's join in, too!'

So they rapped with a pitter
and a pit-pit-pat.
And they rapped with a rappety
rat-tat-tat.

And they rapped all day
and they rapped all night.
And you never ever saw
such a pit-pat-rip-rap
pitter-patter-ripper-rapper
rappety-clappety-rip-rap sight!

Cynthia Rider

September Shoe Rap

De only good ting
bout back to school
is buying new shoes
and playing de fool.

September here,
summer garn,
mi trainers off
mi new shoes on!

Mi mum say Gial
ya playin no more
keep bright, black shoe
from nine till four.

From nine till four
I sit in school,
but on mi way home
I forget de rules.

I run in de grass
kick up de dust
mi bright, black shoe
their shine don't last.

Mi mum see mi shoe,
she look real mean.
She get out de cloth
and make me clean.

I polish mi shoe
till they shine bright.
Me new black shoes
make September all right.

Chris Riley

Write-a-rap Rap

Hey, everybody, let's write a rap.
First there's a rhythm you'll need to clap.
Keep that rhythm and stay in time,
cause a rap needs rhythm and a good strong rhyme.

The rhyme keeps coming in the very same place
so don't fall behind and try not to race.
The rhythm keeps the rap on a regular beat
and the rhyme helps to wrap your rap up neat.

'But what'll we write?' I hear you shout.
There ain't no rules for what a rap's about.
You can rap about a robber, you can rap about a king,
you can rap about a chewed-up piece of string . . .
(well, you can rap about almost . . . anything!)

242

You can rap about the ceiling, you can rap about the floor,
you can rap about the window, write a rap on the door.
You can rap about things that are mean or pleasant,
you can rap about wrapping up a Xmas present.

You can rap about a mystery hidden in a box,
you can rap about a pair of smelly old socks.
You can rap about something that's over and gone,
you can rap about something going on and on and on and
    on . . .

But when you think there just ain't nothing left to say . . .
you can wrap it all up and put it away.
It's a rap. It's a rap. It's a rap rap rap rap RAP!

Tony Mitton

Recipe poems

A recipe poem is a poem written in the form of a recipe.

Making the Countryside

Take a roll of green,
Spread it under a blue or blue-grey sky,
Hollow out a valley, mould hills.

Let a river run through the valley,
Let fish swim in it, let dippers
Slide along its surface.

Sprinkle cows in the water-meadows,
Cover steep banks with trees,
Let foxes sleep beneath and owls above.

Now, let the seasons turn,
Let everything follow its course,
Let it be.

June Crebbin

Nightmare Recipe

Mix a nightmare
Stir a nightmare
Pour in all your fears,
Add a shake of darkness
And several drops of tears.

Ingredients
- Creaking stairs and floorboards
  When you're all alone.
- The monster of the fireplace
  Who watches from the stone.
- The unseen angry creature
  Who whistles round the house.
- The scurrying night-time footsteps
  You're just hoping is a mouse!
- Skeletons and tree roots,
  Cobwebs in your hair,
- Torches without batteries
  And a dead fish stare.

Mix it well, your nightmare
Then throw it all away.
Wash it up, your mixing bowl
Ready for the day!

Daphne Kitching

Recipe for Spring

Some sunny warm days,
a soft-bustling breeze.

Scatterings of swallows
and greening of trees.

Soapsud-white clouds
in a bluebell sky.

Rain sprinkling freshness.
A splash in my eye!

Ducklings and daisies
and buzzing of bees.

Blustery beaches
and freshly made cheese.

Off to the park
to run, slide and swing.

It's the best of all seasons,
welcome back, Spring!

Joan Poulson

Rhyming poems

There are many different types of rhyming poems. The pattern of rhymes in a verse or poem can be described by giving each rhyme a letter. A rhyming poem which has verses of four lines each may have one of these rhyme-schemes: either aaaa , abcb, abba, aabb or abab.

Finding a Dragon's Lair

The way to find a dragon's lair
is down the road that goes nowhere,
over the bridge of Curse-and-Swear
on the river of Deep Despair.

Take the track to Give-You-A-Scare
across the marsh of Say-A-Prayer,
over the peak of Past Repair
and down the cliff of Do Beware.

Through the valley of If-You-Dare
you'll find the town of Don't-Go-There
where folk won't speak but stand and stare
and nobody will be Lord Mayor.

Beyond lies land that's parched and bare,
a dried-up lake named None-To-Spare,
a rock that's known as Life's Unfair
and hills they call No-Longer-Care.

It's hard to breathe the dreadful air
and in the sun's relentless glare
the heat becomes too much to bear.
You'll not be going anywhere.

You're weak and dazed but just aware
of something moving over there
approaching to inspect its snare.
And then you smell the dragon's lair.

Nick Toczek

Queen Nefertiti

Spin a coin, spin a coin
  All fall down;
Queen Nefertiti
  Stalks through the town.

Over the pavements
  Her feet go clack,
Her legs are as tall
  As a chimney stack.

Her fingers flicker
  Like snakes in the air,
The walls split open
  At her green-eyed stare.

Her voice is thin
    As the ghosts of bees
She will crumble your bones,
    She will make your blood freeze.

Spin a coin, spin a coin,
    All fall down;
Queen Nefertiti
    Stalks through the town.

Anon.

Ernie – A Cautionary Tale

Ernie watched so much TV
He put down roots in the settee.
At night he never went to bed.
He vegetated there instead.

He stared and stared, hour after hour.
His face became a pale white flower.
Green leaves sprouted from his hair.
He drove his parents to despair.

His mother fetched a watering can.
'You'll never grow into a man,'
She sighed and, sprinkling him with care,
She pulled some weeds out of his hair.

Louisa Fairbanks

November

The leaves are fading and falling,
  The winds are rough and wild,
The birds have ceased their calling,
  But let me tell you, my child,

Though day by day, as it closes,
  Doth darker and colder grow,
The roots of the bright red roses
  Will keep alive in the snow.

And when the Winter is over,
  The boughs will get new leaves,
The quail come back to the clover,
  And the swallow back to the eaves.

The robin will wear on his bosom
  A vest that is bright and new,
And the loveliest way-side blossom
  Will shine with the sun and dew.

The leaves today are whirling,
  The brooks are dry and dumb,
But let me tell you, my darling,
  The Spring will be sure to come.

There must be rough, cold weather,
   And winds and rains so wild;
Not all good things together
   Come to us here, my child.

So, when some dear joy loses
   Its beauteous summer glow,
Think how the roots of the roses
   Are kept alive in the snow.

Alice Cary

Windy Nights

Whenever the moon and stars are set,
   Whenever the wind is high,
All night long in the dark and wet,
   A man goes riding by.
Late in the night when the fires are out,
Why does he gallop and gallop about?

Whenever the trees are crying aloud,
   And ships are tossed at sea,
By, on the highway, low and loud,
   By at the gallop goes he.
By at the gallop he goes, and then
By at the gallop he comes back again.

Robert Louis Stevenson

Half Rhymes

Like the picture you show Miss Card
who says, That isn't too bad

Or the scarf you give to Aunt Flower
who says, That isn't my colour

Or when your best friend is playing catch
and she says, If you like you can watch

Or the day you thought wouldn't come
as you walk to school on your own

Roger Stevens

Riddles

A riddle poem is one in which you write about something without telling the reader what it is, so the reader has to solve the riddle by working out the meaning for themselves.

Anonymous Riddles

Riddle 1

Some thing I tell
With never a word;
I keep it well,
Though it flies like a bird.

Riddle 2

In rainy squall or pattering shower,
I open like a sudden flower;
But when the wind blows strong to gale,
I huddle close and furl my sail;
Then, peg-leg hopping down the street,
I follow close my master's feet.

Riddle 3

This coat can be of many colours
But no one's worn it yet.
For you can only put it on
When the coat is wet.

Riddle 4

In marble halls as white as milk,
Lined with a skin as soft as silk,
Within a fountain crystal-clear,
A golden apple doth appear.
No doors are there to this stronghold,
Yet thieves break in and steal the gold.

Riddle 5

I was round and small like a pearl,
Then long and slender, as brave as an earl.
Since like a hermit I lived in a cell.
And now like a rogue in the wide world I dwell.

Riddle 6

In Spring I look gay
Deck'd in comely array,
In Summer more clothing I wear;
When colder it grows
I fling off my clothes,
And in Winter quite naked appear.

Anon.

I Had Four Brothers

I had four brothers over the sea,
And they each sent a present to me.

The first sent a goose without any bone,
The second sent a cherry without any stone.

The third sent a blanket without any thread,
The fourth sent a book that could not be read.

How could there be a goose without any bone?
How could there be a cherry without any stone?

How could there be a blanket without any thread?
How could there be a book that could not be read?

When the goose is in the egg, it has no bone,
When the cherry's in the blossom, it has no stone.

When the wool's on the sheep, it has no thread,
When the book is in the press, it cannot be read.

Anon.

Through a bright autumnal air

Through a bright autumnal air
We fall from grace, and from
The arms that held us.

The brilliant discourse of our veins
Has ended now; our fresh green thoughts
Must gossip with the dead ideas
Of yesterday.

Strewn, we lie at your feet
And when disturbed by shuffling children
Know that even they shall not escape.

John Mole

A Double Riddle

There is one that has a head without an eye,
   And there is one that has an eye without a head.
You may find the answer if you try;
   And when all is said,
   Half the answer hangs upon a thread.

Christina Rossetti

It sifts from leaden sieves

It sifts from leaden sieves,
It powders all the wood,
It fills with alabaster wool
The wrinkles of the road.

It makes an even face
Of mountain and of plain, –
Unbroken forehead from the east
Unto the east again.

It reaches to the fence,
It wraps it, rail by rail,
Till it is lost in fleeces;
It flings a crystal veil

On stump and stack and stem, –
The summer's empty room,
Acres of seams where harvests were,
Recordless, but for them.

It ruffles wrists of posts,
As ankles of a queen, –
Then stills its artisans like ghosts,
Denying they have been.

Emily Dickinson

My First Is in Peapod

My first is in peapod but not in bean.
My next is in orange but not tangerine.
My third is in eggplant and also in grape.
My fourth is in trifle but not found in crêpe.
My fifth is in rhubarb and also in rice.
My last is in yoghurt but never in spice.
  My whole is before you,
  Plain as nose on your face.
  Reason this rhyme out
  And you'll win the race.

John Kitching

Snake Riddle

Why didn't the viper
Vipe 'er nose?
Because the adder
'ad 'er handkerchief.

Anon.

Answers to Riddles:

Anonymous Riddles
Riddle 1: time
Riddle 2: umbrella
Riddle 3: paint
Riddle 4: egg
Riddle 5: frog
Riddle 6: tree

Through a bright autumnal air
leaves

A Double Riddle
pin and needle

It sifts from leaden sieves
snow

My First Is in Peapod
poetry

Rondelets

A rondelet is a seven-line poem in which lines 1, 3 and 7 are the same, and which uses only two rhymes in the pattern abaabba.

I spun a star

I spun a star
Which gleamed and glittered in the night.
I spun a star
And watched it spellbound from afar
Until it disappeared from sight,
A flickering speck of silver light.
I spun a star.

John Foster

Autumn Rondelet

Under the trees
Wind blown branches litter the ground.
Under the trees
Racing, dancing, the season flees,
Summer gone, mist muffles all sound.
In shafts of light leaves twirl around
Under the trees.

Lucinda Jacob

S is for . . .

Shape poems
A shape poem is one in which the arrangement and layout of the words form a shape or picture which represents an aspect of the subject.

Little Acorns

if the oaks tell jokes
if the palm can sing a psalm
if the elm excels at villanelles
if the ash can bash out a sonnet
if the sycamore cares for metaphor
if the weeping-willow trees like similes
if the chestnut's nuts about raps and chants
if the pines and the limes write lines that rhyme
if the hickory's trick is the limerick
if the yew does a cool haiku or clerihew
if the plane can scribble a cinquain
if the apple counts in syllables
if the firs prefer free verse
if the plum makes puns
THEN
LET
THIS
BE MY
POE TREE

David Horner

The Scarecrow

I
AM
USED TO
BEING
A
SCARECROW. BUT SOMETIMES IN SUMMER
I WISH
I COULD
RUN ALONG
THE FIELDS
AND FEEL
THE FRESH
GRASS
UNDER
M
Y
S
T
R
A
W
FEET.

Ruth West

Layers

onions are just like me, you have to peel before you see the many layers deep inside, the parts of me I always hide

Coral Rumble

Tornado!

Tree trunks, tables, tractors tossed like toys,
　　twizzled in the twister, tumbled, tattered
　　　　and tormented by the tearless tearaway,
　　　　　　the untamed tempest with a
　　　　　　　tireless talent for turning
　　　　　　　the terrain into a tapestry
　　　　　　　of terror, as it twists
　　　　　　　and turns, twists
　　　　　　　and turns on
　　　　　　　its tiny
　　　　　　　terrible
　　　　　　　tip!

Tim Pointon

A Ride

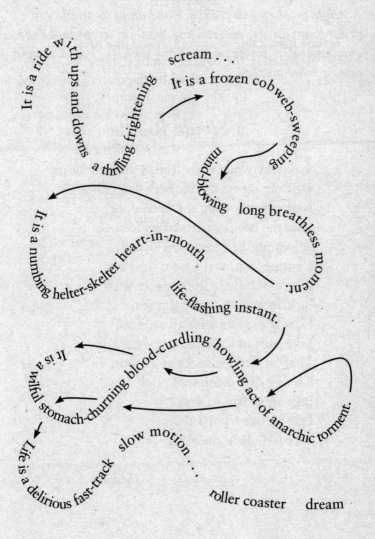

It is a ride with ups and downs a thrilling frightening scream . . . It is a frozen cobweb-sweeping mind-blowing long breathless moment. It is a numbing helter-skelter heart-in-mouth life-flashing instant. It is a blood-curdling howling act of anarchic torment. It is a wilful stomach-churning slow motion . . . Life is a delirious fast-track roller coaster dream

Debjani Chatterjee

Simile poems

A simile is when you compare one thing to another in order to create an image, using 'like' or 'as' to make the comparison. A simile poem is one which is based around one or more similes.

A Simile Riddle

Like the white curls from a gigantic beard
Drifting across the barber's shop floor
In the breeze from the open door;
Like the broken parts of an ice floe
Afloat on the blue of the ocean,
Drifting southward from the Pole;
Like a heavily laden treasure fleet
In a light wind on a calm sea,
Hardly moving with all sails set;
Like suds of foam from a waterfall
That lathers the rocks at its foot,
Gliding over a tranquil pool;
Like wool from a fleece,
Like smoke from a fire,
Like islands in the sky.

Stanley Cook

Starlings

This cold grey winter afternoon
The starlings
On the television aerial
Look like sultanas
On a stalk.

Lucy Hosegood

Cats

Eyes like emeralds
Beautiful as jewels
Claws like hooks
Prowling for the kill –
Cats.

Anon.

Rats

Fur like silk
Grey as ash
Tails like snakes
Sly, curious, deadly –
Rats.

Anon.

The Shape of a Good Greyhound

A head like a snake,
a neck like a drake.
A back like a beam,
a belly like a bream.
A foot like a cat,
a tail like a rat.

Anon.

from *The Destruction of Sennacherib*

The Assyrian came down like the wolf on the fold,
And his cohorts were gleaming in purple and gold;
And the sheen of their spears was like stars on the sea,
When the blue wave rolls nightly on deep Galilee.

Like the leaves of the forest when Summer is green,
The host with their banners at sunset were seen;
Like the leaves of the forest when Autumn hath blown,
The host on the morrow lay wither'd and strown.

Lord Byron

Daisies

Where innocent bright-eyed daisies are,
With blades of grass between,
Each daisy stands up like a star
Out of a sky of green.

Christina Rossetti

Jealousy

Jealousy is like a great black
hole sucking everything
in.
Jealousy is like a fungus
growing and growing inside,
Like a monster punching me inside,
Like a star burning up,
Like a bee-sting right inside –
that's
what
jealousy is.

Terry Baylis

Sonnets

A sonnet is a poem with 14 lines, each of which has 10 syllables and the same iambic pattern of stressed and unstressed syllables. Sonnets can have a variety of different rhyme schemes. The most common are the Shakespearean: abba cdcd efef gg; and the Petrarchan: abbaabba cdcdcd.

Upon Westminster Bridge

Earth has not anything to show more fair:
  Dull would he be of soul who could pass by
  A sight so touching in its majesty:
The City now doth, like a garment, wear
The beauty of the morning; silent, bare,
  Ships, towers, domes, theatres, and temples lie
  Open unto the fields, and to the sky;
All bright and glittering in the smokeless air.
Never did sun more beautifully steep
  In his first splendour, valley, rock, or hill;
Ne'er saw I, never felt, a calm so deep!
  The river glideth at his own sweet will:
Dear God! the very houses seem asleep;
  And all that mighty heart is lying still!

William Wordsworth

Ozymandias

I met a traveller from an antique land
Who said: 'Two vast and trunkless legs of stone
Stand in the desert . . . Near them, on the sand,
Half sunk, a shattered visage lies, whose frown,
And wrinkled lip, and sneer of cold command,
Tell that its sculptor well those passions read
Which yet survive, stamped on these lifeless things,
The hand that mocked them, and the heart that fed.
And on the pedestal these words appear:
"My name is Ozymandias, King of Kings:
Look on my works, ye Mighty, and despair!"
Nothing beside remains. Round the decay
Of that colossal wreck, boundless and bare,
The lone and level sands stretch far away.'

Percy Bysshe Shelley

Bournemouth: September 3rd, 1939

My summer ends, and term begins next week.
Why am I here in Bournemouth with my aunt
And 'Uncle Bill', who something tells me can't
Be really my uncle? People speak
In hushed, excited tones. Down on the beach
An aeroplane comes in low over the sea
And there's a scattering as people reach

For towels and picnic gear and books, and flee
Towards the esplanade. Back at the hotel
We hear what the Prime Minister has said.
'So it's begun.' 'Yes, it was bound to.' 'Well,
Give it till Christmas.' Later, tucked in bed,
I hear the safe sea roll and wipe away
The castles I had built in sand that day.

Anthony Thwaite

The Soldier

If I should die, think only this of me:
That there's some corner of a foreign field
That is for ever England. There shall be
In that rich earth a richer dust concealed;
A dust which England bore, shaped, made aware,
Gave, once, her flowers to love, her ways to roam,
A body of England's, breathing English air,
Washed by the rivers, blest by suns of home.

And think, this heart, all evil shed away,
A pulse in the eternal mind, no less
Gives somewhere back the thoughts by England given;
Her sights and sounds; dreams happy as her day;
And laughter, learnt of friends; and gentleness,
In hearts at peace, under an English heaven.

Rupert Brooke

Return from School Camp

I stare through glass and hear the engine's roar
As, jolting down the lane, our coach makes tracks.
We shudder to a road we've travelled before;
A week has passed and now we must go back.
We leave behind our cabins made of wood,
The warming fires we lit, the rafts we made,
The mud that fell from boots just where we stood,
The maps we followed through the forest glade.
We take with us the memories of camp,
The echoes of the lunch hall and the night,
The smiles seen in the glow of night-time lamps,
The knowledge that we managed things just right.
   But now I stare and stare through windowpane,
   Eager to touch the love of home again.

Coral Rumble

Spells

A spell is a poem written in the form of a spell.

A Spell to Cure Sorrow and to Create Joy

Take the whisper of the river,
The thunder of the sea,
The echo of the songbird,
The rustle of the tree,
The howling of the blizzard,
The purring of the cat,
The shudder of the earthquake,
The whistle of the gnat,
The rumble of the stormcloud,
The singing of the sun,
The music of the moonrise,
And mix them one by one,
Till all the notes are silver
And all the chords are gold.

Then give your gift of laughter
To the sick, the sad, the old.

Clare Bevan

Spells

I crackle and spit. I lick and leap higher.
This is the spell of the raging fire.

I clasp and grasp. I grip in a vice.
This is the spell of torturing ice.

I claw and scratch. I screech and wail.
This is the spell of the howling gale.

I clash and crash. I rip asunder.
This is the spell of booming thunder.

I whisper. I stroke. I tickle the trees.
This is the spell of the evening breeze.

I slither. I slide. I drift. I dream.
This is the spell of the murmuring stream.

John Foster

Spell

By the mound of the moon
And the spikes of the stars
Bring down my sleep onto me.

By circles of Saturn
And the mountains of Mars
Bring down my sleep onto me.

By the deep of the dark
And the silence of streams
Bring down my sleep onto me.

By the hoot of the owl
And the dungeon of dreams
Bring down my sleep onto me.

By the sound of my spell
And the breath on my bed
Bring down my sleep onto me.

Steve Turner

Spell for Spring

I'll weave a spell and send it to
Friend after friend. It will bring you
Spring again with all its show
  Even if it is slow.

I'll cast a spell upon the land
And every field, and it will end
The winter's damage. You will see
  Blossom on every tree.

But there's another spell. It brings
Persephone and all the springs
That she has known.
  She casts a light.

We're dazzled by the sight.

Elizabeth Jennings

A Country Spell Against Witches

Blackthorn bark and poppy seed,
Thistledown and water-weed,
Send the witches off with speed.

Anon.

T is for . . .

Tanka

A tanka is a classical Japanese poetic form, which consists of five lines which together add up to 31 syllables. The syllables are arranged in the following way: 5–7–5–7–7.

Entertainers

Diving, leaping high,
Performing grey clowns frolic
In bottle-nosed fun,
Entertaining the fish world,
Smiling sea stars, the dolphins.

Daphne Kitching

Death of a Dove

White feathers on grass.
A circling hawk high above.
Could he be the one
that dropped like a stone upon
the legendary bird of love?

Ann Bonner

With the Dog

Flip, I feign a throw.
Brink-skidded, he sees my game;
its splashed, ripe redress.
Smash and grab among jewels;
dripping, snout and stick return.

Geoffrey Holloway

Night Sky

Bright stars stud black skies;
Clear-seeing, we gaze amazed;
Winter-chilled but thrilled.
No wonder human beings
Seek to read the face of space.

John Kitching

Tongue-twisters

A tongue-twister is a poem that is difficult to say properly without making a mistake, because it uses similar or repeated sounds.

A Twister of Twists

A twister of twists once twisted a twist,
The twist that he twisted was a three-twisted twist;
If in twisting the twist, one twist should untwist,
The untwisted twist would untwist the twist.

Anon.

Well Swum Swan

Swan swam over the sea,
Swim, swan, swim.
Swan swam back again,
Well swum swan.

Anon.

There's no need to light a night light

There's no need to light a night light
On a light night like tonight;
For a night light's a slight light
On a light night like tonight.

Anon.

A Flea and a Fly in a Flue

A flea and a fly in a flue
Were caught, so what could they do?
Said the fly, 'Let us flee.'
'Let us fly,' said the flea.
So they flew through a flaw in the flue.

Anon.

Shaun Short's Short Shorts

Shaun Short bought some shorts.
The shorts were shorter than Shaun Short thought.
Shaun Short's short shorts were so short,
Shaun Short thought, Shaun you ought
Not to have bought shorts so short.

John Foster

A *Twister for Two Tongues*

'I can can-can.
Can you can-can?'
'Yes, I can can-can, too.
In fact, I can can-can
Very, very well.
I can can-can better than you.'
'No, you can't can-can
better than I can can-can
because I can can-can better!'
'Bet you can't!'
'Bet I can!'
'Bet you can't!'
'Bet I can! I can! I can can-can better!'

Cynthia Rider

Theophilus Thrapplethorn

Theophilus Thrapplethorn,
  The celebrated thistle-sifter,
While sifting a sieve of unsifted thistles
  Thrust three thousand thistles
Through the thick of his thumb.
  If Theophilus Thrapplethorn
The successful thistle-sifter,
  Thrust three thousand thistles
Through the thick of his thumb,

See that thou,
When thou siftest a sieve of thistles,
  Dost not get the unsifted thistles
Stuck in thy thumb!

Anon.

I saw Esau

I saw Esau kissing Kate.
Fact is we all three saw.
I saw Esau, he saw me,
And she saw I saw Esau.

Anon.

Pop Bottles Pop-bottles

Pop bottles pop-bottles
  in pop shops;
The pop-bottles Pop bottles
  poor Pop drops.
When Pop drops pop-bottles,
  pop-bottles plop.
When pop-bottles topple,
  Pop mops slop.

Anon.

Triolets

A triolet is a French verse-form, consisting of eight lines, with the first line and the second line repeated as refrains and that uses only two rhymes in the pattern abaaabab. Lines 1, 4 and 7 are the same and lines 2 and 8 are the same.

My Unicorn

My Unicorn
How Beautiful
In Dew of Dawn
My Unicorn
Washes his Horn
In the Forest Pool
My Unicorn
How Beautiful.

John Whitworth

The Post-box

I'm always open and I hope
That you'll be passing by
Holding a crisp white envelope.
I'm always open and I hope
You'll visit me. I couldn't cope
Without your post. I'd cry.
I'm always open and I hope
That you'll be passing by.

Your letters are my lunch and tea.
Just post them in my mouth
And you'll be sort of feeding me.
Your letters are my lunch and tea.
And then the postman comes and he
Sends them east, west and south.
Your letters are my lunch and tea
Just post them in my mouth.

After the postman leaves, I'm sad
With all my letters gone.
So hurry, find a writing pad.
After the postman leaves, I'm sad.
I want more letters than I had
Before, so please – write on!
After the postman leaves, I'm sad
With all my letters gone.

Sophie Hannah

The Joker

I am the joker in the pack,
The card who makes you smile.
I'm not like King or Queen or Jack,
I am the joker in the pack –
The cheeky one who answers back
And tells you all the while:
'I am the joker in the pack
The card who makes you smile.'

Colin West

Valentine

My heart has made its mind up
And I'm afraid it's you.
Whatever you've got lined up,
My heart has made its mind up
And if you can't be signed up
This year, next year will do.
My heart has made its mind up
And I'm afraid it's you.

Wendy Cope

U is for . . .

Ultimatum poems

An ultimatum poem is one in which the poet lists the final warnings, or ultimatums, issued by someone, e.g. a parent or a teacher.

My mum says

My mum says:

If you don't pick up your pyjamas
and fold them under your pillow,
I'll throw them out of the window
for the binmen to pick up.

If you don't go upstairs
and get washed immediately,
I'll take you out into the garden
and turn the hosepipe on you.

If you don't hurry up and get dressed,
I'll take you to school
in your knickers.

If you're not out of this door
in ten seconds' time,
I'll kiss you goodbye outside school.

My mum says:

You think I'm joking, don't you!

John Foster

Threats

'Unless you let me through,' said the wind,
'I will batter all night at your door.
I will tear up your trees by the roots
And rip the slates from your roof.'

'Unless you treat me with respect,' said the fire.
'I will devour your forests with my flames.
I will set light to your homes
And reduce them to smouldering ruins.'

'Unless you watch your step,' said the ice.
'I will make you dance to my tune.
I will make you slither and slide
And fall flat on your face.'

John Scotby

Univocalics

A univocalic is a poem which uses only words containing one of the five vowels.

Low Owl

Cold morn: on fork of two o'clock
Owl's hoot flows from hood of wood.

Owl's song rolls from blood to brood,
Owl's hoot loops onto top of town roofs,
Owl's song swoops on strong doors.

Owl's slow whoop – long, forlorn –
soft flood of moon song.

John Rice

Anna's All-star Band

Anna has a band –
Anna's band raps raps –
Madcap ragbag claptrap raps.

Sharks snap jaws
Jackals jam jazz
Crabs clap claws –
Razzmatazz.

Llamas chant psalms
Swans twang saws
Carps clasp harps
And cats tap paws.

Ants bang pans
Rats rat-a-tat
A calf cancans
And yaks yak-yak.

Anna has a band –
Anna's band raps raps –
Madcap ragbag claptrap raps.

John Scotby

September Elms

Three deer tremble by the September elms
      where scree defends tree.
   Reeds jerk where the creek ebbs.

Here the kestrel preens herself:
tree-queen, she freewheels the skyless sphere,
   never seeks her sweet eye-sleep.

Her fever screech skewers her prey.

John Rice

V is for . . .

Villanelles

*A villanelle is a French verse form consisting of 19 lines
arranged in five three-line verses and a final four-line verse.
Only two rhymes are used. Line 1 is repeated in lines 6, 12
and 18 and line 3 is repeated in lines 9, 15 and 19.*

Villanelle

A dainty thing's the Villanelle;
   Sly, musical, a jewel in rhyme,
It serves its purpose passing well.

A double-clappered silver bell
   That must be made to clink in chime,
A dainty thing's the Villanelle.

And if you wish to flute a spell,
   Or ask a meeting 'neath the lime,
It serves its purpose passing well.

You must not ask of it the swell
   Of organs grandiose and sublime –
A dainty thing's the Villanelle;

And filled with sweetness, as a shell
   Is filled with sound, and launched in time,
It serves its purpose passing well.

Still fair to see and good to smell
   As in the quaintness of its prime,
A dainty thing's the Villanelle,
It serves its purpose passing well.

William Ernest Henley

Villanelle

King Arthur stands, the archetypal male,
Spanning the centuries to our present age,
Searching forever for the Holy Grail.

Epitomising, by his mythic tale,
Honour and chivalry: on every page
King Arthur stands, the archetypal male.

He, with his knights, rides through the forest trail
Ready with wars or women to engage,
Searching forever for the Holy Grail.

In sunshine, lightning, thunder, snow or hail,
Wherever good men just and true wars wage,
King Arthur stands, the archetypal male.

From the Round Table forth, in shining mail
See Arthur lead his knights, with that old sage,
Searching forever for the Holy Grail.

With such support, how could he ever fail?
And yet he died; but still, where battles rage,
King Arthur stands, the archetypal male,
Searching forever for the Holy Grail.

Pam Gidney

Witch Villanelle

This night as I lie in my shadowed bed
I watch the moon in her cloudy shawls
And dream alone inside my head.

It's Hallowe'en when fear is spread,
My wide-awake ears hear screech owl calls,
This night as I lie in my shadowed bed.

The clock strikes twelve, twelve chimes to dread.
I hear footsteps creak where a moonbeam falls
And dream alone inside my head.

I think I hear Moon-witches tread
And birch-horses stamp in their daytime stalls,
This night as I lie in my shadowed bed.

Far off to the dark wood the moon has fled.
I think of a tattered witch and trolls
And dream alone inside my head.

Though now from the sky no light is shed,
I see black cats leaping garden walls,
This night as I lie in my shadowed bed
And dream alone inside my head.

Catherine Benson

The World Is Dark When All My Friends Grow Cold

The world is dark when all my friends grow cold,
And icy stares show no sign of a thaw,
And even Ben believes the lies he's told.

The gossip is protected like it's gold
And each will add to it a little more
The world is dark when all my friends grow cold.

The hurtful lies soon grow a hundredfold.
I hear my name when passing by each door,
And even Ben believes the lies he's told.

Now all the fragile memories I hold
Of loyal friends are broken on the floor;
The world is dark when all my friends grow cold.

I realize my secrets have been sold,
My heart is rubbed with sadness till it's raw.
And even Ben believes the lies he's told.

Mum says that I must learn to be more bold,
Dad says life's tough, I have to know the score;
But the world is dark when all my friends grow cold,
And even Ben believes the lies he's told.

Coral Rumble

'Villa-nelle

If only I could play for Aston Villa,
I've got the kit – the claret and the blue,
I'd quash the opposition like Godzilla.

Every game would be a real thriller,
I'd show them how to score a goal or two,
If only I could play for Aston Villa.

The fans would find a nickname like 'Gorilla'
For me, as the pitch became a zoo.
I'd quash the opposition like Godzilla.

Their goalie would be crying in his pillow,
I'd make him think he hadn't got a clue,
If only I could play for Aston Villa.

They'd look at me and say, 'Here comes The Killer,'
Though I may get shown a red card, that is true.
As I quashed the opposition like Godzilla.

But, for now, I'll lick my strawberry and vanilla
Ice-lolly, while I'm waiting in the queue
To see the lads that play for Aston Villa
Quash the opposition like Godzilla.

Celia Warren

W is for . . .

Warnings

A warning poem is a poem written in the form of a warning.

Superstitions

Wash your hands in the moonlight,
don't step on any crack;
cross your fingers,
cross your toes,
touch wood to keep your luck.

Always watch for black cats,
wear odd socks unawares;
choose sevens or threes,
'Bless you!' when you sneeze,
and never cross on stairs.

Remember these with all you've got;
      if not . . .

Judith Nicholls

If You Should Meet a Crocodile

If you should meet a crocodile
　　Don't take a stick and poke him;
Ignore the welcome in his smile,
　　Be careful not to stroke him.
For as he sleeps upon the Nile,
　　He thinner gets and thinner;
But whene'er you meet a crocodile
　　He's ready for his dinner.

Anon.

Be careful of the porcupine

Be careful of the porcupine
a rodent archer by design
a bowman with a bull's-eye quill
an armoury that moves at will.

Be wary of the porcupine
a dangerous quiver for a spine
do not approach or cause him to
direct his weapons straight at you.

Be kindly to the porcupine
his back's so sharp, he can't recline
do not go close and make him tense
he only fires in self defence.

Stewart Henderson

Beware the Draculasaurus

Beware the Draculasaurus
Who roams graveyards at night.
Don't let him grab you by the throat.
He's thirsty for a bite!

The other dinosaurs are dead.
Their bones have turned to stone.
Only Draculasaurus lives –
A monster all alone.

His bloodshot eyes glow in the dark,
His fingernails are claws.
Beware his razor teeth.
Beware his slavering jaws.

As he lurks behind the tombstones,
The moon glints on each scale.
He's waiting there to wrap you up
In his forked serpent's tail.

Beware the Draculasaurus
Who roams graveyards at night.
Don't let him grab you by the throat.
He's thirsty for a bite!

John Foster

Wishes

A wish is any poem that expresses some kind of a wish.

Starlight, Star Bright

Starlight, star bright,
First star I've seen tonight;
I wish I may
I wish I might
Get the wish I wish tonight.

Anon.

Youth and Age

Impatient of his childhood,
  'Ah me!' exclaimed young Arthur,
While roving in the wild wood,
  'I wish I were my father!'
Meanwhile, to see his Arthur
  So skip, and play and run,
'Ah me!' exclaims the father,
  'I wish I were my son!'

Thomas Hood

Tiger Shadows

I wish I was a tiger in the Indian jungle
The jungle would be my teacher.

No school
And the night sky a blackboard smudged with stars
I wish I was a tiger in the Indian jungle

Kitten-curious
I'd pad about on paws as big as frying pans

While the monkeys chattered in the trees above me
I'd sniff the damp jungly air
Out of exotic flowers I would make a crown of pollen

If I were a tiger in the Indian jungle
My eyes would glitter among the dark green leaves
My tail would twitch like a snake

I would discover abandoned cities
Where no human feet had trod for centuries

I would be lord of a lost civilisation
And leap among the vine-covered ruins

I wish I was a tiger in the Indian jungle
As the evening fell
I'd hum quiet tiger-tunes to which the fireflies would dance
I'd watch the red, bubbling sun
Go fishing with its net of shadows

While the hunters looked for me miles and miles away
I'd lie stretched out in my secret den

I would doze in the strawberry-coloured light
Under the golden stripy shadows of the trees
I would dream a tiger's dream

Brian Patten

Wings

If I had wings
   I would touch the fingertips of clouds
     and glide on the wind's breath.

If I had wings
   I would taste a chunk of the sun
     as hot as peppered curry.

If I had wings
   I would listen to the clouds of sheep bleat
     that graze on the blue.

If I had wings
   I would breathe deep and sniff
      the scent of raindrops.

If I had wings
   I would gaze at the people
      who cling to earth's crust.

If I had wings
   I would dream of
     swimming the deserts
       and walking the seas.

Pie Corbett

Wish

Clasp in your hand
the single black feather
left in your garden
as a gift from a crow.

Whisper the words
that you learned from the wind.

Find dragonfly's spit
and a snake's shed skin.

Find a flower's heartbeat
and the moon's lost silver.

Now gather them together
with the crow's black feather . . .

And WISH . . .

Brian Moses

Wordplay poems

A wordplay poem is any poem that plays with words and/or their meanings.

The Ptarmigan

The ptarmigan is strange
As strange as can be;
Never sits on ptelephone poles
Or roosts upon a ptree.
And the way he ptakes pto spelling
Is the strangest thing pto me.

Anon.

Life Is Butter

Life is butter, life is butter;
Melancholy flower, melancholy flower;
Life is but a melon, life is but a melon
Cauliflower, cauliflower.

Anon.

The Word Wizard Said

Start with yourself:
I
Add the first letter of tag
And become the chaser:
It
Now take an e, shuffle and make a knot:
Tie
Insert an r and become weary:
Tire
Put in a p, stir and get some food
That is not to everyone's taste:
Tripe
Add an s and get one in line:
Stripe
Or a ghostly spirit
Sprite
Add another e, stir again
And get a break from these puzzles:
Respite.

John Foster

Driven to Distraction

I picked up a bus in the High Street
then put it down on the park,
I drove my Mum to Distraction –
that's the next town on from Dunkirk.

I stood, like a lemon, in a downpour
and someone gave me a squeeze,
I gave the cold shoulder to Matthew,
in minutes it started to freeze.

I got into hot water for fibbing,
the water didn't tell me a thing,
I threw bread at a tree for a lark
but instead it decided to sing.

I turned up my nose at the dinner,
it stayed like that for a week,
I tried not to be a wet blanket,
but my shoe laces started to leak.

Chrissie Gittins

Where?

Where do you hide a leaf?
in, if possib*le*, *a f*orest.

where do you hide a wind?
among stra*w*, *in d*ust.

where do you hide a horse?
within clo*th or se*a.

where do you hide the sun?
behind cloud*s*, *un*der horizons.

where do you hide water?
belo*w a ter*rible flood.

where do you hide a storm?
inside a gho*st or m*agician.

where do you hide a word?

Dave Calder

X *is for* . . .

X-ray poems

An X-ray poem is a poem which explores beneath the outer surface of a subject or subjects to reveal what's inside in the way that an X-ray can reveal the bones inside your body.

Inside the Morning

Inside the morning is a bird,
Inside the bird is a song,
Inside the song is a longing.

And the longing is to fill the morning.

June Crebbin

Windows

I looked through windows made of ice
And saw the swarms of silver fish
Flutter and flick away. Zig, zig
Through water white as albumen,
Water green as frozen spears.

I looked through windows made of leaves
Where paintbox parrots scream and flap
Where emerald snakes seem limbs of vines
Siss, wind and slide in strangling creepers.
Where bees and dragons burn and sting
While blood red flowers eat the steaming air.

I looked through windows made of bread
And saw the yellow eyes of men
Saw too many yellow bones
The yellow hunger of their skin.
They stood in long slow lines and starved
I saw them there but didn't let them in.

Jan Dean

Inside a Shell

Inside a shell
There is the whisper of a wave.

Inside a feather
There is the breath of a breeze.

Inside an ember
There is the memory of a flame.

Inside a rock
There is the murmur of a mountain.

Inside a well
There is the echo of a wish.

Inside a seed
There is the promise of a flower.

John Scotby

In My Mind's Eye

I saw the caged bird
flying free in the sunlit sky.

I saw the pacing bear
loping across the Arctic ice.

I saw the hunted fox
nuzzling her cubs in her den.

I saw the bloodied seal
somersaulting in the waves.

I saw the refugee child
skipping across a village square.

I saw the homeless vagrant
digging in the garden of his home.

I saw the tortured prisoner
dancing in a carnival procession.

I saw the lifeless soldier
cradling his newborn son.

Louis Johnson

Behind the Raised Eyebrow

Behind the raised eyebrow
I glimpsed a host of silent questions.

Behind the scornful grin
I heard the snigger of derision.

Behind the tearstained cheeks
I tasted the salt of wasted wishes.

Behind the odour of sweat
I smelt the scent of fear.

Behind the touch of a hand
I felt the faint stirrings of hope.

Eileen Pickersgill

Y is for . . .

Yearnings

A yearning poem is a poem which expresses a yearning or longing of some kind.

Home-thoughts, from Abroad

Oh, to be in England
Now that April's there,
And whoever wakes in England
Sees, some morning, unaware,
That the lowest boughs and the brushwood sheaf
Round the elm-tree bole are in tiny leaf,
While the chaffinch sings on the orchard bough
In England – now!

And after April, when May follows,
And the whitethroat builds, and all the swallows!
Hark, where my blossomed pear-tree in the hedge
Leans to the field and scatters on the clover
Blossoms and dewdrops – at the bent spray's edge –
That's the wise thrush; he sings each song twice over,
Lest you think he never could recapture
The first fine careless rapture!
And though the fields look rough with hoary dew,
All will be gay when noontide wakes anew
The buttercups, the little children's dower
– Far brighter than this gaudy melon-flower.

Robert Browning

A Wanderer's Song

A wind's in the heart of me, a fire's in my heels,
I am tired of brick and stone and rumbling wagon-wheels;
I hunger for the sea's edge, the limit of the land,
Where the wild old Atlantic is shouting on the sand.

Oh I'll be going, leaving the noises of the street,
To where a lifting foresail-foot is yanking at the sheet;
To a windy, tossing anchorage where yawls and ketches
     ride,
Oh I'll be going, going, until I meet the tide.

And first I'll hear the sea-wind, the mewing of the gulls,
The clucking, sucking of the sea about the rusty hulls,
The songs at the capstan at the hooker warping out,
And then the heart of me'll know I'm there or thereabout.

Oh I am tired of brick and stone, the heart of me is sick,
For windy green, unquiet sea, the realm of Moby Dick;
And I'll be going, going, from the roaring of the wheels,
For a wind's in the heart of me, a fire's in my heels.

John Masefield

My Heart's in the Highlands

My heart's in the Highlands, my heart is not here;
My heart's in the Highlands a-chasing the deer,
Chasing the wild deer and following the roe,
My heart's in the Highlands wherever I go.
Farewell to the Highlands, farewell to the North,
The birth-place of valour, the country of worth,
Wherever I wander, wherever I rove,
The hills of the Highlands for ever I love.

Farewell to the mountains, high covered with snow;
Farewell to the straths and green valleys below;
Farewell to the forests and wild-hanging woods;
Farewell to the torrents and loud-pouring floods.
My heart's in the Highlands, my heart is not here;
My heart's in the Highlands a-chasing the deer;
Chasing the wild deer and following the roe,
My heart's in the Highlands, wherever I go.

Robert Burns

Sing Me a Song of a Lad That Is Gone

Sing me a song of a lad that is gone,
 Say, could that lad be I?
Merry of soul he sailed on a day
 Over the sea to Skye.

Mull was astern, Rhum on the port,
 Eigg on the starboard bow;
Glory of youth glowed in his soul;
 Where is that glory now?

Sing me a song of a lad that is gone,
 Say, could that lad be I?
Merry of soul he sailed on a day
 Over the sea to Skye.

Give me again all that was there,
 Give me the sun that shone!
Give me the eyes, give me the soul,
 Give me the lad that's gone!

Sing me a song of a lad that is gone,
    Say, could that lad be I?
Merry of soul he sailed on a day
    Over the sea to Skye.

Billow and breeze, islands and seas,
    Mountains of rain and sun,
All that was good, all that was fair,
    All that was me is gone.

Robert Louis Stevenson

from *Poem of Joys*

O to sail to sea in a ship,
To leave this steady, unendurable land,
To leave the tiresome sameness of the streets, the sidewalks
    and the houses;
To leave you, O you solid motionless land, and entering a
    ship,
To sail and sail and sail!

Walt Whitman

Z is for . . .

Zoo-plaque poems

A zoo-plaque poem is a poem which takes a form similar to the written description of an animal, giving details of its name, country of origin, habitat and habits that you see on the cage in a zoo. The form was developed by the Cuban poet, Nicholas Guillen, who imagined that everything in the world was in a zoo and wrote plaques for various cages.

Hunger

This is hunger. An animal
all fangs and eyes.
It cannot be distracted or deceived.
It is not satisfied with one meal.
It is not content
with a lunch or a dinner.
Always threatens blood.
Roars like a lion, squeezes like a boa,
thinks like a person.

The specimen before you
was captured in India (*outskirts of Bombay*),
but it exists in a more or less savage state
in many other places.

Please stand back.

Nicholas Guillen

Fright

Fright is a very scared creature
With wide eyes and a pale face.
It shivers day and night,
Cold and clammy.
You can hear the chattering teeth
As it creeps towards you.
Beware!
For we are all victims of this animal.

Madeleine Bentley

Time

This creature is elusive.
It slips by you
In the blink of an eye.
Its tracks stretch endlessly
Backwards into the past,
And eternally forward into the future.
Scientists measure it
In light years,
Athletes in fractions of seconds.
Watch out!
There it goes!

John Foster

An A–Z of Ideas for Writing

Acrostics (pages 3–6)
- Read Cynthia Rider's poem 'Waterfall' (p.3). Notice how she includes a lot of alliteration – the use of several words together that all begin with the same letter(s) or sounds. Write your own acrostic about a natural feature, e.g. thunder, tornado, volcano. See if you can include some alliteration.
- Write an acrostic in which one of these words is formed: school, teacher, lessons, homework, tests, reports.
- Look at 'Whoosh! Cheetah!'(p.4) and 'The Bard' (p.5) Write a similar acrostic which forms the name of an animal or a famous person.

Adverb poems (pages 7–10)
- Use Aenaone Tickler's poem 'Quietly'(p.7) as a model and write a similar poem. Either choose an adverb yourself or choose one from this list: slowly, gently, softly, swiftly, brightly.
- Write an adverb poem using the same pattern as Erica Stewart's 'Suddenly' (p.7).

Advertisement poems (pages 11–14)
- Draft a Wanted poem advertising for a person to do an unusual or dangerous job, such as a wizard's apprentice, a spy or a pirate. Include all the qualities the person must have.
- Write an advertisement poem in which a toy advertises

for a new home because it is no longer wanted by its owner.

Alphabet poems (pages 15–19)
- Read Wes Magee's poem 'An A–Z of Pop Groups' (p.16), then write your own A–Z poem, e.g. An A–Z of Horror Movies, An A–Z of Space Creatures.
- Write your own alphabet word-play poem in which you play with the sounds made by each of the letters. You could use the following as the first two lines of your poem: Ate nine canaries / Before I had a swim . . .

Autobiographical poems (pages 20–24)
- Read John Mole's 'What It Was Like' (p.20). Think of a time when something frightening has happened to you and write a poem based on that experience.
- Remember a time when you had very strong feelings – perhaps you were very happy, very embarrassed, very sad or very disappointed. Use the memory as the basis of an autobiographical poem.

Ballads (pages 27–35)
- Draft a ballad which tells a story of some kind – for example about a famous historical event, such as the Gunpowder Plot, about a famous sporting event or sports personality, or about a sensational news story, such as a dramatic rescue. Start with a verse saying either where and when the event happened or who or what the ballad is going to be about.

Calligrams (pages 39–43)
- Look at Ian Bland's 'Calligrams' (pp.40–41). Notice how the way the letters are formed or positioned reflects the meaning of each of the words, then draft some calligrams of your own. Either choose your own words or use some of these: bubbles, shivering, hopping, earring, descending, disintegrating.

Chain poems (pages 44–49)
- Read 'If a Jackal Bothers You' (p.45). Think of words which you could put instead of 'bothers' in each line, then write your own chain poem giving advice on what to do if certain animals or people bother you, e.g. If a dog snarls at you . . .
- Write a chain poem about one of the following: The pearl of wisdom, the feather of truth, the fountain of hope or the snowflake of peace.

Chants (pages 50–53)
- Write a chanting poem that begins 'Teacher, teacher/it wasn't me'.
- Read 'The Witches' Chant' (p.53). Use it as a model and write a chant called 'The School Cook's Chant'.

Cinquains (pages 54–58)
- Write a cinquain about a particular person, animal or object, e.g. a soldier or a conjuror, a fox or an elephant, a computer or a statue.
- Draft a sequence of cinquains of your own. For example, you could write about a day at school, a

special day, e.g. a festival or celebration, or a bus, train or plane journey.

Clerihews (pages 59–61)
- Write one or two clerihews of your own. You could write about a historical person, a famous celebrity, one of your friends or family, or a made-up person such as Felicity Fish or Deborah Drain.

Colour poems (pages 62–66)
- Use Christina Rossetti's poem 'What is pink?' (p.62) as a model and write a similar poem about various different colours.
- Read 'I Asked the Little Boy Who Cannot See' (p.64) and write a poem which consists of comparisons between colours and things you hear, smell, taste or touch.

Column poems (pages 67–70)
- Write a column poem set in a classroom, describing what is going on in a lesson in the left-hand column and a girl's or boy's thoughts in the right-hand column.
- Read 'False Alarm' (p.70). Remember a time when you have been alarmed and frightened because you have mistaken an object or a sound for something dangerous, in the way that the boy in the poem does. Develop your own column poem about such an experience.

Concrete poems (pages 71–74)
- Design some concrete poems of your own in which you use the layout of the word or words to suggest a feature

of the subject. Either think of your own subject or choose one of these – lighthouse, firework, padlock, tambourine.

Conversation poems (pages 75–80)

- Write a poem in which either a parent is questioning a child about something they have done, urging a child to hurry up or refusing to allow a child to do something.
- Read 'What's Your Name?' (p.75) and make up some extra verses, e.g. What's your name? / Tobias Toad. / Where do you live? / Rhubarb Road . . .

Counting poems (pages 81–87)

- Make up your own counting rhyme similar to 'One Old Oxford Ox' (p.81), e.g. you could begin it: 'One obstinate owl offering ogres oranges . . .'
- Write a counting rhyme which, like 'Ten Green Bottles', counts down from ten to one, e.g. Ten Silly Schoolchildren.

Couplets (pages 88–92)

- Write a poem in rhyming couplets. Either choose your own subject or write about an unusual experience using these two lines to start your poem:
  A strange thing happened yesterday
  When my friend and I went out to play.

Diamond poems (pages 95–96)

- Look at 'Two Diamond Poems'(p.95). Notice how both of them describe an action of some kind. Then draft a diamond poem of your own describing an action, e.g. a bomb exploding, a volcano erupting, a rocket-launch, a road accident.

Diary poems (pages 97–100)
- Read 'The Secret Diary of a Dragon' (p.97). Write a poem consisting of the secret diary entries of another mythical creature, e.g. an elf, an ogre or a troll, or of an alien or space beast.

Elegies (pages 103–107)
- Write an elegy either for someone who sacrificed their life for others, e.g. a fire officer or lifeboatman, who died in a rescue attempt, or a member of the armed forces who was killed in action.
- Read 'Elegy for a Much-loved Dog' (p.104), then write an elegy for an animal which has died.

Epigrams (pages 108–109)
- Notice how most of the epigrams consist of a single rhyming couplet. Try to write an epigram of your own. Make a list of proverbs – wise sayings that provide guidance on or state a commonplace fact, e.g. shutting the stable door after the horse has bolted; once bitten, twice shy; patience is a virtue. Then try to present one of them as a couplet.

Epitaphs (pages 110–114)
- Draft an epitaph for a famous historical figure or for someone whose name suited their occupation, e.g. a

caretaker called Mrs Broom, a butcher called Mr Chop, a gardener called Mr Flower or a footballer called Gerry Goal.
- Read 'Nursery Epitaphs' (p.111) then write a number of epitaphs about popular cartoon characters such as Mickey Mouse.

Fables (pages 117–122)
- Either think of any traditional fables you know or find a fable in a book from your library, e.g. *Aesop's Fables*. Then re-tell the fable in a poem.

Greetings (pages 125–129)
- Imagine you wake up to find that it has snowed heavily overnight. Write a greetings poem welcoming the snow.

Haiku (pages 133–136)
- Write a series of haiku about animals, e.g. pets haiku, zoo haiku or farmyard haiku. Try to make them each say something about the character of the animal you are describing.
- An effective haiku is often like a snapshot describing a scene or capturing a particular moment or feeling. Write one or two haiku describing scenes, e.g at the seaside or at a football match, or capturing particular emotions, e.g. fear, joy, guilt.

Insults (pages 139–143)
- Use the poem 'You!' (p.139) as a model. Write a similar

poem in which you use a number of comparisons to insult somebody.

- Read Eric Finney's 'Vocabulary for Villains' (p.143) and use some of the adjectives he includes to write 'the vilest poem ever'.

Interviews (pages 144–146)

- Write a poem in the form of an interview. Your interview can be with anything you choose from a football to a toothbrush, from a tractor to an elephant.

Joke poems (pages 149–152)

- Think of jokes you have heard recently. Try to turn one of them into a four-line joke poem.
- Read 'As the Witch Said to the Skeleton' (p.150). Write a similar poem either 'As the Waiter Said to the Diner' or 'As the Teacher Said to the Pupil'.

Kennings (pages 155–157)

- Read Daphne Kitching's 'Two Kennings' (p.156–7) then write a similar kenning poem about another animal.
- Use Steve Turner's 'Sun' (p.155) and June Crebbin's 'River' (p.156) as models and write your own kenning poem about subjects such as moon, hurricane, sea or fire.

Letter poems (pages 161–164)

- Read Paul Cookson's poem 'Dear Headteacher' (p.161). Then write your own letter poem making excuses for something you've done, such as being late or forgetting

346

your homework. You can make your excuses as far-fetched as you like!

- Write a letter poem addressed to your mum apologizing for all the things you haven't done but should have done and/or all the things you do but she wishes you wouldn't do.

Limericks (pages 165–168)

- Read David McCord's 'The Limerick' (p.168), then draft a limerick of your own. Either make up your own first line or use one of these:

  There once was a teacher called Pool . . .
  A wizard's apprentice called Nell . . .
  There once was a dentist called Jill . . .

List Poems (pages 169–174)

- Read Sue Cowling's 'Quiet Things' (p.169), then write your own list poem about soft things, bright things or smooth things.
- Write a list poem describing the sounds you might hear in a city street, at a train station or lying in your bed at night. You could begin your poem with this line: 'Listen can you hear . . .'

Lullabies (pages 175–179)

- Notice how the poets in this section use rhythm and rhyme to create a soothing effect. Either use one of them as a model and draft your own version of it or write a lullaby beginning with the line 'Sing a song of dream-time'.

Metaphor poems (pages 183–186)

- Write a metaphor poem about a machine of some kind, e.g. a mechanical digger, a crane, an aeroplane, a lawn mower, a carpet sweeper, a telephone or a computer.

Nonsense poems (pages 189–195)

- Read 'YUMMY!' (p.190), then write some extra verses about other animals and the foods they like. You could begin one of the extra verses like this: 'Cheetahs like chocolates . . .'
- Read 'The Num-Num Bird' (p.189), then write a poem about a nonsensical animal such as The Hulkabaloo or The Kettle Fish.

Odes (pages 199–201)

- Read 'To a Skylark' (p.199) and 'To a Butterfly' (p.200). Draft an ode addressed to another creature, e.g. to a robin or a penguin, a squirrel or a hamster, a mouse or a rabbit.

Parodies (pages 205–209)

- Read 'Alternative Nursery Rhymes' (p.208). Make a booklet of 'Alternative Nursery Rhymes' including any other alternative nursery rhymes that you have heard and ones that you make up yourself.

Postcard poems (pages 210–212)

- Imagine you are on a camping or caravanning holiday where lots of things go wrong. Write a 'Wish you were here' postcard poem addressed to a relative or friend.

- Read 'Postcards in 23 Words' (p.211) and write some similar postcards to add to the poem, e.g. Postcard from a Desert Island, Postcard from the Jungle, Postcard from the Wizard's Cave.

Poster poems (pages 213–214)

- Write a 'Vote for me' poster poem in which an animal expresses the reasons why it should get your vote in an election, e.g. a mouse from the Ban Mousetraps Party, a canary from the Free to Fly Party or a whale from the Anti-Whaling Party.
- Write a 'Do Not Disturb' poster for a dragon to put up outside its cave.

Prayers (pages 215–220)

- Write a prayer poem from someone who is either praying for rain to fall to bring an end to a drought or praying for rain to stop in order for flooding to stop.
- Read 'Spring Prayer' (p.217), then write an 'Autumn Prayer' giving thanks for the harvest.

Puns (pages 221–224)

- Make a list of words with similar sounds but different meanings, e.g. bread/bred, hoarse/horse, pair/pear, rain/rein/reign, stares/stairs, wait/weight and another list of words which are spelled the same but have different meanings, e.g. bark, stamp. Then try to draft a humorous poem based on a pun or a number of puns.

Question poems (pages 227–233)

- Remind yourself what an anagram is. Read 'A Ragman's Puzzle' (p.230) and draft one or two extra verses for the poem.

Raps (pages 237–243)

- Read 'Write-a-rap Rap' (p.242). Then choose a subject and write your own rap. A good way of getting ideas for your rap is to note down any words connected with the subject which rhyme. For example, here is the start of a list of rhymes for a football rap: score-draw-roar; boot-shoot . . .

Recipe poems (pages 244–246)

- Write your own recipe poem. Either choose your own subject or select a subject from this list: a dragon, a pirate, a haunted house, a disco, a fair. Start by brainstorming all the ingredients you will need for whatever you are making. Then draft your poem in the form of instructions for a recipe.

Rhyming poems (pages 247–252)

- Notice how each of the poems in this section has a different rhyme pattern from the others. Focus on Louisa Fairbanks's poem 'Ernie – A Cautionary Tale' (p.249). Write your own cautionary tale, e.g. about someone who never washes or someone who eats too many sweets. Either use the rhyme pattern Louisa Fairbanks uses (aabb) or the rhyme pattern of 'Queen Nefertiti' (abcb) (p.248).

Riddles (pages 253–259)

- Use John Kitching's 'My First Is in Peapod' (p.258) as a model and draft a similar poem in which the reader has to solve the riddle by picking out the letter in each line that spell the word which is the subject of the poem. Either choose your own subject or one from this list: television, lemonade, football, ladder, computer.
- Study John Mole's 'Through a bright autumnal air' (p.256). Notice how he describes the subject of the poem without ever naming it. Draft a similar poem in which you describe something without ever naming it, e.g. a train, the sea, the wind, a volcano.

Rondelets (page 260)

- Read 'Autumn Rondelet' (p.260) and write a rondelet about either spring, summer or winter.

Shape poems (page 263–267)

- Read Ruth West's poem 'The Scarecrow' (p.264). Notice how she imagines the scarecrow can speak and how she arranges the words it says to make the scarecrow's shape. Draft a poem in which an object or creature expresses its thoughts and feelings and present it as a shape poem by arranging the words inside the object's or creature's shape.

Simile poems (pages 268–271)

- Write a poem similar to 'Jealousy' (p.271) in which you use a number of similes to describe an emotion such as joy, fear, guilt, hope or sadness.

- Read 'Cats' and 'Rats' (p.269). Use them as models to write some five-line poems in which you use a number of similes to describe the characteristics of different animals.

Sonnets (pages 272–275)

- Write a sonnet in which you describe your thoughts and feelings during or after a particular experience, as Coral Rumble does in her poem 'Return from School Camp' (p.275).

Spells (pages 276–279)

- Write your own spell poem. It could be a spell to protect you from something or someone, e.g. a giant or a tiger, or a spell to banish fear. Or it could be a spell to create something, e.g. a spell to bring snow, or a spell to create peace. You could develop your poem as a list as Clare Bevan does in her poem 'A Spell to Cure Sorrow and to Create Joy' (p.276).

Tanka (pages 283–284)

- Choose an animal and write a tanka which describes the animal in the way that Daphne Kitching does in 'Entertainers' (p.283).
- Write a tanka which describes a particular scene, e.g. at a football stadium, at a train station, at a fair or in a market.

Tongue-twisters (pages 285–288)

- Tongue-twisters are often difficult to say because they

play with the sounds of words, using alliteration – the repetition of the same sound at the beginning of several words. Draft a tongue-twister of your own. For example, you could focus on words that begin with the letters ch and write a tongue-twister about a cheeky chicken.

Triolets (pages 289–291)

- The triolet is a difficult form, because you are not only restricted to two rhymes but you also have to repeat lines. Either think of a subject yourself or try writing about one of these subjects: night, Christmas Day, the sea.

Ultimatum poems (pages 295–296)

- Use John Foster's poem 'My Mum Says' (p.295) as a model and write a similar poem, either 'My Dad Says' or 'My Teacher Says'.

Univocalics (pages 297–298)

- These are very difficult to write, because you are so restricted, being able to include only words containing one of the five vowels. Choose a vowel and start by making a list of words that only have that vowel in them. Show your list to other people and get them to suggest words too. Then study the list and try to find several words that can be connected together to give you a first line and start to draft your poem.

Villanelles (pages 301–306)

- This is another difficult form to use, because of the restrictions and the repetitions. Study Celia Warren's poem ''Villa-nelle' (p.305). Use it as a model to write a similar poem, e.g. If only I could play for Man. United.

Warnings (pages 309–311)

- Make up a name for a monster, then write a poem about it, as John Foster has done in 'Beware the Draculasaurus' (p.311).
- Write a poem that is a warning not to go to a dangerous place. Either develop an idea of your own or use one of these suggestions:

  Do not follow the track that leads . . .

  Never go down those steps . . .

  Do not unfasten the heavy oak door . . .

Wishes (pages 312–316)

- Read Pie Corbett's poem 'Wings' (p.314). Use it as a model and write your own poem 'If I could breathe beneath the sea . . .'
- Study Brian Patten's 'Tiger Shadows' (p.313). Which animal would you choose to be, if you had a choice – a butterfly, a seal, a polar bear, a swan? Choose the animal that you would wish to be and write a poem beginning 'I wish I was . . .'

Wordplay poems (pages 317–320)

- Study 'The Word Wizard Said' (p.318). Notice how the poet builds up a word letter by letter starting with 'I' and ending with 'respite'. Write a similar poem starting with any other letter from the alphabet and try to build up to a word consisting of six or seven letters.

X-ray poems (pages 323–326)

• Write an X-ray poem. Develop an idea of your own or draft a poem which begins with one of these suggestions:
Behind the old oak door . . .
Inside the cat's eyes . . .
Beyond the gate . . .

Yearnings (pages 329–333)

• Write a poem describing the thoughts of a city-dweller who longs for the peace of the countryside or a country person who longs for the excitement of the city.

Zoo-plaque poems (pages 337–338)

• Write a zoo-plaque poem of your own, giving details of your animal's character and appearance, where it can be found, what its habitat is and what its habits are. Your subject can be anything from shyness and hope to terrorism and suspicion, from peace and patience to greed and dishonesty.

Index of First Lines

Index of First Lines

Index of Poets

Acknowledgements

The compiler and publisher wish to thank the following for permission to use copyright material:

Andrew, Moira, 'Rainbows' from *Rainbow Year*, Belair Publications, 1994, by permission of the author; **Benson, Catherine,** 'Witch Villanelle' from *The Poetry Store*, Hodder Children's Books, 2005, by permission of the author; **Benson, Gerard,** 'Riddle-me-right' and 'Gorse' from *Evidence of Elephants*, Viking, 1995, 'Postcards in 23 Words' from *To Catch an Elephant*, by permission of the author; **Berry, James,** 'Haiku Moments' by permission of the author; **Bevan, Clare,** 'A Spell to Cure Sorrow and to Create Joy' by permission of the author; **Black, Matt,** 'Alphabotsie, Alphaboodle' and '6 shy haiku found hiding in the oaks in Parkin Woods' by permission of the author; **Bonner, Ann,** 'Death of a Dove' by permission of the author; **Brownjohn, Sandy,** 'Nine Lives' from *Both Sides of the Catflap*, Hodder, 1996, by permission of the author; **Calder, Dave,** 'Where?' by permission of the author; **Caley, Richard,** 'Wanted!!' 'Postcard from School Camp', from *Bats, Balls and Balderdash*, Durrington Press Ltd, 1998, by permission of the author; **Carter, James,** 'Icy Morning Haiku' by permission of the author; **Chatterjee, Debjani,** 'A Ride' from *What Shape Is a Poem?* ed. Paul Cookson, Macmillan, 2002, by permission of the author; **Cook, Stanley,** 'Tyrannosaurus Rex' and 'A Simile Riddle' by permission of his literary executors; **Cookson, Paul,** 'Trick or Treat' from *Trick or Treat*, Macmillan, and 'Dear Headteacher' from *Loony Letters and Daft Diaries*, Macmillan, both by permission of the author; **Cope, Wendy,** 'Valentine' from *Serious Concerns*, Faber and Faber, by permission of the author; **Corbett, Pie,** 'Wings' by permission of the author; **Cowling, Sue,** 'Quiet Things' and 'Song Thrush Poster' both by permission of the author; **Crebbin, June,** 'Cathedral' and 'Inside the Morning' from *Cows Moo, Cars Toot*, Viking, 1995, and 'River' and 'Making the Countryside' all by permission of the author; **Davis, W. H.,** 'A Greeting', from *Selected Poems*, Jonathan Cape, by permission of his literary estate; **Dean, Jan,** 'Windows' from *Nearly Thirteen*, Blackie, 1994, by permission of the author; **Desmond, John C.,** 'Interview with Mr Crabman, Superhero' by permission of the author; **Douthwaite, Gina,** 'Wild Bear/Tame Bear' from *An Armful of Bears*, Methuen, 1992, and 'How Do I Feel?' from *I'm in a Mood Today*, Oxford University Press, 2000, by permission of the author;

Acknowledgements

Doyle, Cornelius, 'Advertisement' from *This Poem Doesn't Rhyme*, Puffin, 1990, by permission of the author; Edwards, Richard, 'Lower the Diver', 'The Holly and the Ivy' and 'Copped' all by permission of the author; Fairbanks, Louisa, 'Ernie – A Cautionary Tale', by permission of John Foster; Finney, Eric, 'Vocabulary for Villains' from *The Evil Doctor Mucus Spleen and other Superbad Villains*, ed. Paul Cookson, Macmillan, 2001, and 'Punishment' from *Another Third Poetry Book*, ed. John Foster, Oxford University Press, 1988, both by permission of the author; Forbes, Sean, 'Column Poems', 'Vowel Play', 'I'm Telling You' and 'In the Cave' by permission of John Foster; Foster, John, 'Di Knows What's Best for Dinosaurs', 'The Castle on the Hill', 'Edmund Clerihew Bentley', 'Colour Story – from Gold to Silver', 'C', 'Crocodile One, Alligator Two', 'Two Diamond Poems', 'Drift Upon a Dream', 'The Sea', 'A Ragman's Puzzle', 'This Poem Has Class', 'I spun a star', 'Spells', 'Shaun Short's Short Shorts', 'My mum says', 'Beware the Draculasaurus', 'The Word Wizard Said' and 'Time' all by permission of the author; Gidney, Pam, 'Villanelle' by permission of the author; Gittins, Chrissie, 'Driven to Distraction' from *Now You See Me, Now You . . .* , Rabbit Hole Publications, 2002, by permission of the author; Hannah, Sophie, 'The Post-box' from *The Box Room*, Orchard, 2001, by permission of the author; Harmer, David, 'Two Traffic Wardens Talking on Christmas Eve' by permission of the author; Harrison, Michael, 'In the Stable: Christmas Haiku' by permission of the author; Harvey, Trevor, 'Rhythm Machine' from *Word Whirls*, ed. John Foster, Oxford University Press, 1998, by permission of the author; Haselhurst, Maureen, 'Back Track, Cycle Rack' from *Words to Whisper, Words to Shout*, ed. Michaela Morgan, Belitha Press, 2002, by permission of the author; Henderson, Stewart, 'Be careful of the porcupine' from *All Things Weird and Wonderful*, Lion, 2003, by permission of the author; Holder, Julie, 'A Letter to the Alphabet' by permission of the author; Holloway, Geoffrey, 'With the Dog' by permission of the estate of the author; Horner, David, 'Little Acorns' from *So There!*, Apple Pie Publications, by permission of the author; Jacob, Lucinda, 'Autumn Rondelet' from *The Poetry Store*, ed. Paul Cookson, Hodder, 2005, by permission of the author; Jennings, Elizabeth, 'Spell for Spring' from *A Spell of Words*, by permission of David Higham Associates on behalf of the author; Johnson, Louis, 'In My Mind's Eye' by permission of John Foster; Kitching, Daphne, 'Two Kennings', 'Nightmare Recipe' and 'Entertainers' from *As Long as There Are Trees*, Kingston Press, 2001, by permission of the author; Kitching, John, 'Nursery Epitaphs', 'Letter to an

Acknowledgements

Unknown Father', 'My First Is in Peapod' and 'Night Sky' all by permission of the author; **Larmont, Ian,** 'Family Doctor' from *Fiendishly Funny Poems*, ed. John Foster, Harper Collins, 2004, by permission of the author; **MacRae, Lindsay,** 'Lonely Heart' by permission of the author; **Magee, Wes,** 'Whoosh! Cheetah!' 'an A–Z of Pop Groups' by permission of the author; **Masefield, John,** 'A Wanderer's Song' by permission of the Society of Authors as the literary representative of the estate of John Masefield; **Millum, Trevor,** 'The Song of the Homeworkers' from *Warning – Too Much Schooling can Damage Your Health* by permission of the author; **Mitton, Tony,** 'The Ballad of Homeless Jack' and 'Write-a-rap Rap' from *My Hat is All That*, Corgi Yearling, 2006, by permission of the author; **Mole, John,** 'Slowly' from *Hot Air*, Hodder, 'What It Was Like' from *The Wonder Dish*, Oxford University Press, 'Through a bright autumnal air' from *Boo to a Goose*, Peterloo Poets, 1987, all by permission of the author; **Moon, Pat,** 'Goodbye' and 'A Message from a Long-serving Member of the Brown Party' by permission of the author; **Morgan, Michaela,** 'YUMMY!' by permission of the author; **Moses, Brian,** 'Wish' from *Taking Out the Tigers*, Macmillan, 2005, by permission of the author; **Nicholls, Judith,** 'What Is One?' from *Storm's Eye*, Oxford University Press, 1994, 'Harvest Hymn' from *What on Earth . . . ?*, Faber and Faber, 1989, and 'Superstitions' from *Midnight Forest*, Faber and Faber, 1989, all by permission of the author; **Ousbey, Jack,** from 'Resting Pets' by permission of the author; **Patten, Brian,** 'The Lion and the Echo' from *Gargling with Jelly*, Puffin, 1985, and 'Tiger Shadows' from *Juggling with Gerbils*, Puffin, 2000, both by permission of the author; **Peters, Andrew Fusek,** 'Thank You (it's what I've always wanted)' from *Mad, Bad and Dangerously Haddock: The Best of Andrew Fusek Peters*, Lion, 2006, by permission of the author; **Petty, Noel,** 'David Attenborough' by permission of the author; **Pickersgill, Eileen,** 'This Is a Troll-bridge' and 'Behind the Raised Eyebrow' by permission of John Foster; **Pointon, Tim,** 'Tornado' from *The Poetry Store*, ed. Paul Cookson, Hodder, 2005, by permission of the author; **Poulson, Joan,** 'Recipe for Spring' by permission of the author; **Rice, John,** 'The Poet Interviews an Electricity Pylon' and 'Low Owl' from *Bears Don't Like Bananas*, Simon & Schuster, 1991, and 'September Elms' all by permission of the author; **Richardson, Kim,** 'Cinderella' and 'Macbeth' both by permission of the author; **Rider, Cynthia,** 'Waterfall' from *The Way Through the Woods*, Oxford University Press, 2000, 'The Fox and the Crow' and 'The Palace Rap' from *Ready, Steady, Rap*, Oxford University Press, 2001, and 'A Twister for Two Tongues' from *Teasing*

Acknowledgements

Tongue Twisters, Collins, 2002, all by permission of the author; **Riley, Chris**, 'September Shoe Rap' from *Unzip your Lips*, ed. Paul Cookson, 1998, by permission of the author; **Rock, Lois**, 'Autumn Treasure' from *What Will You Wear To Go Swimming?* by Lois Rock, Lion Hudson plc, 2002, by permission of Lion Hudson plc; **Rumble, Coral**, 'Acrostics', 'Sad School Cinquains', 'Layers' and 'Return from School Camp' from *Breaking the Rules*, Lion, 2004, 'Seasonal Cinquains' from *Frogs in Clogs*, ed. Gaby Morgan, Macmillan, 2005, 'The World Is Dark When All My Friends Grow Cold' from *Mice on Ice*, ed. Gaby Morgan, Macmillan, 2004, and 'Postcard from the Garden Shed' all by permission of the author; **Scotby, John**, 'The Pole Star', 'Threats', 'Anna's All-star Band', and 'Inside a Shell' by permission of John Foster; **Sedgwick, Fred**, 'Mr Khan's Shop' from *Blind Date*, Tricky Sam! Press, 1998, by permission of the author; **Simmons, Sheila**, 'The Secret Diary of a Dragon' by permission of the author; **Smith, Doda**, 'The Num-Num Bird' by permission of the author; **Stevens, Roger**, 'Alien Love Poems', 'Mother's Day Prayer' and 'Half Rhymes' from *Why Otters Don't Wear Socks*, Macmillan, by permission of the author; **Stewart, Erica**, 'Suddenly', 'How wickedly the wolf grins', 'Extract from a Reindeer's Diary' and 'Steam Train' all by permission of John Foster; **Stuart, Derek**, 'The Bard', 'Animal Noises' and 'ice cube' all by permission of John Foster; **Swinger, Marian**, 'Three Limericks' by permission of the author; **Thwaite, Anthony**, 'Bournemouth: September 3rd, 1939', from *Collected Poems*, Enitharmon Press, 2007, by permission of the publisher; **Toczek, Nick**, 'Seasick' and 'Finding a Dragon's Lair' by permission of the author; **Turner, Steve**, 'Sun' and 'Spell' from *The Day I Fell Down the Toilet*, Lion, 1996, by permission of the author; **Tysoe, Richard**, 'The Nest That Jack Built' by permission of the author; **Warren, Celia**, 'Left Out' from *Feelings*, ed. John Foster, Oxford University Press, 1995, 'Football Training' from *They Think It's All Over*, ed. David Orme, Macmillan, 1998, ''Villa-nelle', from *Football Fever*, ed. John Foster, Oxford University Press, 2000, all by permission of the author; **Webster, Clive**, 'You Remind Me of the Sea' by permission of the author; **West, Colin**, 'The Joker' by permission of the author; **West, Ruth**, 'The Scarecrow' by permission of the author; **Whitworth, John**, 'My Unicorn' by permission of the author; **Yates, Irene**, 'Shopping List for a Fireworks Display' by permission of the author.

Every effort has been made to trace the copyright holders but if any have been inadvertently overlooked the publishers will be pleased to make the necessary arrangement at the first opportunity.

Every kind of poem you will
ever need for assembly

Chosen by Pie Corbett

From poems about faith, the environment, happiness and
friendship to poems about loss and conflict. There are
poems to celebrate achievement and poems to help us
deal with the times we live in.

A book packed with gems for dipping into
time and time again.

A selected list of titles available from Macmillan Children's Books

The prices shown below are correct at the time of going to press.
However, Macmillan Publishers reserves the right to show new retail prices
on covers, which may differ from those previously advertised.

Read Me 1	978-0-330-37353-1	£6.99
Read Me 2	978-0-330-39132-0	£6.99
Read Me and Laugh	978-0-330-43557-4	£6.99
Read Me Out Loud	978-0-330-44621-1	£6.99
The Works	978-0-330-48104-5	£6.99
The Works 2	978-0-330-39902-9	£6.99
The Works 3	978-0-330-41578-1	£6.99
The Works 4	978-0-330-43644-1	£6.99
The Works 5	978-0-330-39870-1	£5.99
The Works 6	978-0-330-43439-3	£6.99
The Works 7	978-0-330-44424-8	£6.99
The Works Key Stage 1	978-0-330-43947-3	£5.99
The Works Key Stage 2	978-0-330-43949-7	£5.99

All Pan Macmillan titles can be ordered from our website,
www.panmacmillan.com, or from your local bookshop
and are also available by post from:

Bookpost, PO Box 29, Douglas, Isle of Man IM99 1BQ
Credit cards accepted. For details:
Telephone: 01624 677237
Fax: 01624 670923
Email: bookshop@enterprise.net
www.bookpost.co.uk

Free postage and packing in the United Kingdom